Perversions

*Psychodynamics
and Therapy*

Perversions

Psychodynamics and Therapy

Edited by

SANDOR LORAND, M.D.

Associate Editor

MICHAEL BALINT, M.D.

Random House

NEW YORK

The Contributors

FRANZ ALEXANDER, M.D. Member, Chicago Psychoanalytic Society; American Psychoanalytic Association; International Psychoanalytical Association · Director, Institute for Psychoanalysis, Chicago · Clinical Professor of Psychiatry, University of Illinois · Fellow, Center for Advanced Study in the Behavioral Sciences

CATHERINE LILLIE BACON, M.D. Member, Philadelphia Psychoanalytic Society; American Psychoanalytic Association; International Psychoanalytical Association · Associate Professor, University of Pennsylvania Graduate School of Medicine

ROBERT C. BAK, M.D. Member, New York Psychoanalytic Society; American Psychoanalytic Association; International Psychoanalytical Association · Secretary, New York Psychoanalytic Institute

MICHAEL BALINT, M.D., Ph.D., M.Sc. Member, British Psychoanalytical Society; International Psychoanalytical Association · Chairman, Medical Section, British Psychological Society · Consultant Psychiatrist, Tavistock Clinic, London

GUSTAV BYCHOWSKI, M.D. Member, New York Psychoanalytic Society; American Psychoanalytic Association; International Psychoanalytical Association · Associate Clinical Professor of Psychiatry, New York University College of Medicine · Associate Visiting Neuro-Psychiatrist, Bellevue Hospital

HANS CHRISTOFFEL, M.D. Member, Swiss Psychoanalytical Society; International Psychoanalytical Association · Member (late Chairman), Swiss Psychological Society · Chairman, Basle Psychological Working Community

LUDWIG EIDELBERG, M.D. Member, New York Psychoanalytic Society; New York Psychoanalytic Association (Vice-President); American Psychoanalytic Association; International Psychoanalytical Association · Clinical Associate Professor of Psychiatry, State University Medical Center, College of Medicine, New York

v

SANDOR S. FELDMAN, M.D. Member, New York Pschoanalytic Society; American Psychoanalytic Association; International Psychoanalytical Association · Associate Professor of Psychiatry, University of Rochester School of Medicine and Dentistry, Psychiatric Department

WILLIAM H. GILLESPIE, M.D., M.R.C.P., D.Psych. Member, British Psychoanalytical Society (late President) · Vice-President, International Psychoanalytical Association · Chairman, London Institute of Psychoanalysis · Consultant Physician, Royal Bethlem and Maudsley Hospitals

WLADIMIR GRANOFF, M.D. Member, Société Française de Psychanalyse · Attaché, Clinique des Maladies Mentales de la Faculté de Médecine de Paris · Médecin de l'Office Public d'Hygiène Sociale, Département de Prophylaxie Mentale

BELA GRUNBERGER, Dr. en med., Lic. es sc soc. Member, Société Psychanalytique de Paris; International Psychoanalytical Association · Director, Seminaire de l'Institut Psychanalytique de Paris

JACQUES LACAN, M.D. Chairman, Société Française de Psychanalyse · Médecin des Hôpitaux Psychiatriques · Former Chief of Clinics, Faculté de Médecine de Paris

RITSKE LE COULTRE, M.D. Member, Dutch Psychoanalytical Society; International Psychoanalytical Association

SANDOR LORAND, M.D. Member, New York Psychoanalytic Society (late President); New York Psychoanalytic Association (President); American Psychoanalytic Association; International Psychoanalytical Association · Clinical Professor of Psychiatry and Director, Division of Psychoanalytic Education, State University Medical Center, College of Medicine, New York

MILTON L. MILLER, M.D. Member, Psychoanalytic Society of Southern California; American Psychoanalytic Association; International Psychoanalytical Association · President, Institute for Psychoanalytic Medicine of Southern California · Senior Attending Physician, Los Angeles County General Hospital Department of Psychiatry

WARNER MUENSTERBERGER, Ph.D. Clinical Assistant, Professor in Psychiatry, State University Medical Center, College of Medicine, New York

GERHARD RUFFLER, Dr.med., Dr.theol. Member, German Society for Psychotherapy and Depth Psychology · Assistant, Psychosomatic Institute, University of Heidelberg

This book is dedicated to
ERNEST JONES, M.D.

Honorary President of the International Psychoanalytical Association, of whom Freud said:
"Not only is he unquestionably the leading man
among English-speaking analysts, but his
knowledge is among the foremost of all representatives of psychoanalysis."

Introduction

THE NEED for such a symposium had occurred to me some time ago as the indirect result of a discussion with Dr. Sandor Feldman concerning the difficulties our younger colleagues encounter when treating patients for perverse sexual practices. These difficulties are due mainly to the younger analysts' lack of proper experience; many of them have not had the opportunity, during the years of their psychoanalytic training, to analyze such patients under the supervision of teachers more experienced in dealing with perversions. They have had to rely on their reading of the literature, which gives some hints about therapeutic techniques but which deals mainly with theories of the psychodynamics, classification and formulation of perversions.

The result of this situation has been that the younger analyst does not accept patients whose difficulties are of a perverse nature, or that, very soon after these patients start analysis, they are dismissed, or that they change from one analyst to another.

Indeed, such patients offer a great challenge to the therapist's skill. Throughout the years of indulging in perverse practices, they have built up so many obstacles to their deep desire for heterosexual gratification that their unconscious and even, in some cases, partly conscious longing for heterosexuality is fought with many conscious and many more unconscious defenses.

This volume offers the reader a summary of current views on

perversion. Although the individual papers in it are, in each case, the free expression of the opinions of their contributors, an attempt has been made to bring some unity into the expression and emphasis of the theoretical, genetic, and therapeutic approaches of the writers.

All the contributors to this volume accept as valid Freud's formulations on perversions. Many of them, however, point out additional factors which play major roles in the etiology of perversions. In addition to the mechanisms of identification, narcissism and penis-envy, which were described by the earlier writers, studies of the pre-Oedipal phases of development—aggression, early anxieties, guilt—make possible a widened and enriched understanding of the psychopathology and etiology of perversions and offer valuable hints about problems of therapy.

I believe the reader will find in this volume many stimulating and helpful ideas about the highly complex problem of perversions.

SANDOR LORAND

Contents

I

General Problems

A Note to the Theory
of Perversions

FRANZ ALEXANDER

A comprehensive theory of perversions should rest on a comprehensive theory of sexuality. This does not need to contain a statement concerning the "ultimate nature" of sexuality. The nature of light is still problematic; yet the laws of optics are well established.

Let us consider at first the cornerstones of the psychoanalytic theory of sexuality in general and that of perversions in particular.

1. The mature forms of sexual instinct develop from early infantile forms.

2. The early manifestations of sexuality do not serve propagation (race preservation). They are localized in parts of the body other than the genitals and are connected with physiological functions which are not related to propagation.

3. These early modalities of sexual excitation are retained to a degree by the mature organism as activities preparatory to the sexual act (fore-pleasure).

4. The mature genital and pregenital manifestations of sexuality can be subjectively well differentiated from other psycho-

logical and physiological phenomena which serve self-preservation or, to use a more recent terminology, serve homeostasis,
the maintenance of stable (optimal?) conditions in the organism under which life is possible. These functions are called,
interchangeably, self-preservative functions, ego-instincts, adaptive or homeostatic functions. The separation of self-preservative functions from sexuality is most clearly seen when they are
in conflict with each other. (Example: the nuptial flight of ter-
mites leading to the death of those participating in it.)

5. Subjectively, sexual activity, both infantile and mature, is
connected with a specific kind of pleasure sensation which is
distinct and can be differentiated, at least in intensity and in its
emotional connotation, from other gratifying experiences such
as esthetic or moral satisfaction. The specific quality of this
intense pleasure sensation was, to a large degree, what induced
Freud to postulate the sexual nature of such infantile practices
as thumb-sucking (oral eroticism) and of certain anal activities
(anal eroticism). Less obvious is the sexual connotation of
pleasure which accompanies the playful practice of physiological
functions not serving survival but executed "for their own sake,"
such as the young child's or animal's seemingly aimless exuber-
ant motor activity (muscle eroticism). Another term used in connection with this type of pleasure is "functional pleasure."[8]

Freud's original theory, presented in the *Three Contributions
to the Theory of Sex,* is an attempt to account for these basic
observations by a unified concept.[4] The essence of it is that mature sexuality develops as the progressive integration of elementary instinctual components, until they become unified under the
primacy of the genital functions. In Freud's original discussion,
it is not clear whether he thought that mature sexuality can be
explained merely as the integration of the elementary partial
instincts of whether he assumed that, at puberty, with the

maturation of sex glands, a new element enters into the picture. He stated, however, that a new sexual aim appears at puberty: sexuality becomes object-directed and, with this, it enters "into the service of propagation."

Ferenczi, in his theory of amphymixis, explains mature sexuality entirely as the fusion of the partial instincts.[2]

Perversions in this light appear as "fragments of inhibited development and infantilism" (Freud). The child, by the very nature of his pregenital sexuality, is "polymorphously perverse." Fixation to early forms of sexual expression may be the result of the constitutional intensity of partial instincts; but it may also be reinforced by accidental sexual experiences in infancy or childhood. Such fixations may lead to perversions in adults. Interference in normal psychosexual development, which mostly occurs at the Oedipal barrier, may interrupt the psychosexual maturational process and initiate a regression to early forms of sexual expression (fixation points). This view was elaborated upon by Hanns Sachs.[3]

In such cases, the pregenital partial instincts do not become organically incorporated in their totality in mature genitality, or this incorporation is so loose that, when obstacles occur (i.e., the Oedipus complex), they break up and sexual expression regresses to the phase which characterized it before the partial instincts were integrated. In normal development, pregenital trends which are in excess of what can be utilized in the formation of normal genital sexuality become sublimated (desexualized) and enter into the personality as socially useful trends. "What we call the character of the person is built up to a large extent from the material of sexual excitations. Consequently perverse sexual dispositions of childhood can be esteemed as a source of a number of our virtues" (Freud).[4] A common example is scientific curiosity which arises from the sublimation of infantile scoptophilia. Attitudes such as pity develop as reaction formations against infantile sadism. "Neurosis is the negative of perversion"; that is to say, some of the infantile sexual trends which become neither absorbed and integrated in mature sexuality nor sublimated and then included as integral parts of the ego must, because of their ego-alien nature, become repressed and find modified, symbolic expression in the form of neurotic symptoms.

Freud did not explain why such a surplus of unutilized pregenital trends appears in some adults as perversions, in others becomes repressed and produces neurotic symptoms, and in still others becomes sublimated. He noted, however, the coexistence of both neurotic symptoms and perversions in many adult neurotics; in fact, he claimed "a preponderance of perverse tendencies in the psychoneurotics."

This concept accounts for the intuitively well-known affinity between sublimation and neurosis which often overlap in the same person. Both sublimations and neurotic symptoms are derivatives of aim-inhibited instinctual trends which have not become integral parts of genital sexuality. Neurotic symptoms result when sublimation of these tendencies did not occur. If not sublimated, they retain their ego-alien connotation and can only be expressed in symbolic disguise as symptoms. If they are sublimated, they become assimilated into the ego and find acceptable, and often creative, expression.

In its basic structure, this theory has great similarity to the principle of the preservation of energy in physics. Different physical phenomena—such as heat, mechanical labor, electricity —are considered as different manifestations of energy commutable into each other. The psychoanalytic theory also assumes that *neurotic symptoms, sublimations, perversions* and *genital sexuality* are different expressions of a psycho-physiological quantity: *libido*. The similarity between the physical and psychological theories does not go farther than this, however. An important difference between the two theories is that, while energy can be quantitatively defined and measured and the specific laws of energy transformation can be expressed in mathematical terms, the same does not hold for the concept of libido. The term "psychic energy" can, therefore, be used only in a figurative manner. With this reservation, libido can be considered as an as yet unmeasurable quantity which had one similarity with physical energy, namely, that it is transformable and can have different external manifestations.

That a quantitative relationship exists between these different manifestations of libido is indicated in the complementary relation of sublimated and non-sublimated sexual trends to each other. Persons who have manifest perversions frequently show a conspicuous lack of the sublimated manifestations of the same trend, which appears openly in their sexual behavior. Sexual exhibitionists are often highly inhibited in their ability to make an impression on the sublimated level. They conspicuously neglect their external appearance and are inhibited in such expressive innervations as gesticulation and modulation of speech. Although I have no statistical data available, I found a number of stammerers among them. Others did not have a definable speech defect but had marked difficulty in verbal expression. It appears that the crude exhibition of their genitals is the only way in which they can gratify their need to be noticed.

It is more commonly known that sexual sadists are often weaklings, incapable of forcefully asserting themselves in their relationship to others. Their aggressiveness is pent up because its normal sublimated expression is inhibited; it is discharged in their sexual behavior. A similar observation pertains to pedophiliacs who are extremely inhibited toward women of their own age because of excessive inferiority feelings. Their only outlet, in many cases, is sadistically distorted sexuality against minors.

In the analysis of *voyeurs*, I have been impressed by the conspicuous absence in them of any sublimated expression of curiosity. A counterpart of this observation was provided by a scientist who devoted himself to basic research. His passion, to uncover and disclose the secrets of nature, was a sublimation of sexual curiosity which had become inhibited at an early age; only in late adolescence did he discover the anatomical difference between men and women.

In the history of passive homosexuals, we often find an early frustration of the longing for a strong father figure. This pent-up, unsublimated passive longing is expressed on the sexual level.

In the case of masochism, such a correlation was explicitly stated by Freud: "An individual may, it is true, preserve the whole of a certain amount of his morality alongside his masochism but, on the other hand, a good part of his conscience may be swallowed up by his masochism."[5] Giving heed to this statement, I was impressed by the extreme, sometimes blatant, selfishness sexual masochists display in human relationships. Their need for punishment finds sexualized expression in their masochism and this frees them from the inhibitory effect of their conscience.*

What I have been saying may be summarized in the state-

---

*This observation indicates a quantitative relationship between sublimated and not sublimated manifestations of a trend (instinct) but does not contradict the possibility that the same trend may appear in both forms—sublimated and sexual—simultaneously. Presumably, in such a case, each manifestation should have a lesser intensity than in the rarer cases in which the trend is expressed only sexually or only in sublimated form.

ment that practically every emotional trend—love, curiosity, the need to call attention to one's self, aggressiveness, and the need for suffering—can be expressed in either non-sexual or sexual form. This was recognized by Freud when he wrote:

> . . . sexual excitation arises as an accessory to a long series of internal processes when the intensity of these processes has exceeded certain quantitative limits.[4]

In another place, he made a similar statement:

> Are we to suppose that the different instincts which operate upon the mind but of which the origin is somatic are also distinguished by different qualities and act in the mental life in a manner qualitatively different? This supposition does not seem to be justified; we are much more likely to find the simpler assumption sufficient—namely, that the instincts are all qualitatively alike and owe the effect they produce only to the quantities of excitation accompanying them, or perhaps further to certain functions of this quantity. The difference in the mental effects produced by different instincts may be traced to the difference in their sources. In any event, it is only in a later connection that we shall be able to make plain what the problem of the quality of instincts signifies.[6]

Although in his later contributions to instinct theory Freud did not follow up these leads, they seem to be worth thorough reexamination.

In language we use the same term "love" for both its sexual and sublimated manifestation, thus expressing our intuitive recognition of their affinity. Cruelty means uninhibited aggression against another person; yet the same cruel act may have a different motivational background. A person who cruelly destroys another man's life may do this for an ultimate goal; he robs him or tries to eliminate him as an obstacle interfering with his aims. A sadist's cruelty against his victim has no such utilitarian aspect. Here cruelty is an aim in itself and a source of sexual pleasure; it is not subordinated to another goal. Similarly, a tourist who, when climbing a mountain, loads himself down with a heavy knapsack certainly inflicts upon himself a painful burden; he does so, however, to protect himself against cold and hunger when he arrives at his destination. A sexual masochist tortures himself for no such utilitarian goal; for him suffering is an aim in itself and a source of sexual pleasure.

A person who, when hungry, goes to see what is contained in the refrigerator is not merely satisfying his curiosity; his urge for exploration is subordinated to a utilitarian goal: to find food. The sexual *voyeur*'s curiosity serves no other purpose than that of sexual pleasure.

In the physical manifestations of pregenital sexuality, the same principle can be recognized. Thumb-sucking is highly similar to sucking on the nipple; it is engaged in, however, not for the gratification of hunger but merely for the sensual pleasure which it affords.

Anal practices, too, can be distinguished from anal functions, which have a physiological utility in the elimination of waste products. The "functional pleasure" derived from the wanton practice of locomotor faculties can be seen in little children or in young animals who aimlessly but joyfully romp around. This locomotor activity is not subordinated to any utilitarian goal, such as approaching an object needed for the gratification of biological needs; it is practiced for its own sake.

In his above-quoted statements, Freud refers to the intensity of the cathexis as a differentiating factor between sexual and non-sexual activity. A close scrutiny of the conditions under which an impulse is discharged sexually and non-sexually shows that intensity is not the only criterion. The crucial difference is that, whenever an impulse is carried out in an isolated manner, as an aim in itself, it assumes an erotic or sexual connotation. If the same impulse is subordinated to other goals and becomes an integral part of what French calls a goal structure, it loses its sexual connotation.[3] Aggression subordinated to some utilitarian gain is not sadism; exploration of the environment to satisfy hunger is not scoptophilia; and enduring suffering as a necessary condition to achieve a cherished goal is not masochism. All these emotions assume a sexual connotation only when they are executed *without being subordinated to any other goal, when they are discharged for their own sake.* In other words, sexual activity is a particular form of discharge, characterized by the condition that it is not part of a behavioral structure in which it is subordinated as a preliminary step to an ultimate goal. The same psychological impulse, if it does become part of a goal structure, loses its erotic quality.

In other writings, I have suggested that such isolated emotional discharges occur under conditions which can be defined as states of excess excitation. There is a surplus of motivational cathexis beyond that which is necessary for coordinated utilitarian or self-preservative functions. An excess of oral craving, beyond what is physiologically conditioned by hunger, is precisely what we call oral eroticism. Excessive accumulated aggressive impulse which is not needed for utilitarian aims, aggressiveness which is not necessary for survival, may be discharged in the form of sadism. Such an excess excitation occurs mainly under two conditions: (1) when there is an amount of excitation in excess of what is useful for the total organism in its survival activities, and (2) when excitations which could not be absorbed and included in the structure of the ego, because of a neurotic interruption of normal maturation, find isolated discharge either in the form of perversions or in neurotic symptoms.

The primary sadism of the child, if it becomes repressed and not integrated in the adult sexual drive, in the form of sexual initiative and activity, nor integrated in its sublimated forms as an acceptable component of the ego, in the form of self-assertion or determination, may be retained in its unadulterated form as perverse sexual behavior. The same holds true for all other emotional tensions.

Ferenczi, in his bioanalytical speculations, came to an essentially similar conclusion when he differentiated between the utility function and the pleasure function of all organ systems. In his formulation, all those excitations which are not needed for utility are discharged as pleasure functions (sexuality). The latter are not subordinated to the interest of the organism as a whole but seek their own particular aims.[2]

This surplus theory of sexuality applies well to the manifestation of pregenital trends, which are defined as elementary impulses not yet integrated under the primacy of genitality. To have a general validity, however, it must also apply to genital sexuality.

I have, before this, tried to define genital sexuality as a derivative of the biological trend to growth; it appears at the phase of development when the organism reaches the limits of its growth and is called mature. Reproduction is growth beyond the limits set by individual growth potential.[1] This theory accords well with the biological view which claims that growth and sexuality are closely related.

Gerard defines the relation of growth to reproduction:

> Clearly the dividing line between growth and reproduction . . . is uncertain and broken. Reproduction of cells constitutes growth of the individual; reproduction of individuals . . . growth of the community. Indeed, reproduction might be looked upon as a form of discontinuity or a critical point dividing an otherwise continuous growth process into a series of separate quanta. . . . The simpler forms of reproduction, the division and separation of cells commonly but not always with mitosis, are merely such a punctuated protoplasmic increase.[7]

As I have just said, genital sexuality leading to reproduction can be considered as growth beyond the limits set by individual potential. In this sense, it is an excess of "growth energy" of which no further use can be made in individual development.

The fact that germ plasma remains isolated and does not become an integrated part of the total organism also accords well with our psychological formulations. According to these, the sexual nature of an emotional discharge depends upon a special condition: whether the discharge takes place as an isolated gratification of a tendency, including the genital impulse, which serves as a goal in itself, or whether it becomes a component part of a goal structure which serves the interest of the total organism. Although, in genital sexuality, the partial drives become integrated and subordinated to the goal of propagation, genital sexuality remains a goal in itself and is not necessarily subordinated to other goals. Genital impulses may also become desexualized and, like any other emotional trend, integrated into the total personality; they then find expression in mature love, creativity or some other sublimated form.

Sublimation, accordingly, consists in the desexualization of any pregenital or genital drive. In contrast to neurotic symptoms, it consists in incorporation and harmonious integration of sublimated derivatives of the originally libidinous drives into the organized structure of the ego.

To summarize: the sexual nature of a discharge does not depend upon the quality of the psychological content of a drive but upon the mode of its discharge. Every tendency (drive, urge) can be discharged in a non-sexual and sexual manner. Love, curiosity, exhibitionism, cruelty, the need for suffering and all the practices of the different physiological faculties—if they become parts of a complex integrated goal structure— lose their original erotic connotation. They express in an integrated manner the needs of the organism as a whole. When they are discharged in isolated forms, in which they constitute aims in themselves and are not subordinated to other aims, they retain their erotic quality. Originally—with the exception of the basic, vegetative functions which are automatically regulated —all functions appear in an unintegrated manner and consequently have an erotic libidinal connotation. As the ego develops, these trends are integrated into complex patterns and lose much of their erotic nature. They become what used to be called ego-drives or character trends. That portion of them which remains in excess of what is needed for adaptive—utilitarian, self-preservative, homeostatic—functions retains its sexual connotation. Libidinous trends which on account of inhibition of ego development—that is to say, for pathological reasons— become neither harmoniously included in the personality nor in genital sexuality retain their original form as perversions. The latter, if repressed, appear disguised as neurotic symptoms —the negative of perversions. Integrated patterns under the influence of developmental obstacles may disintegrate; they break up into their isolated components. Such a disintegration of the genital impulse into its component parts is the essential mechanism in perversions (regression). Possibly, in some cases, partial drives never become integrated at all (fixation), retaining their original form appearing as perversions in the adult.

REFERENCES

1 Alexander, Franz. *Fundamentals of Psychoanalysis.* New York, 1948.

2 Ferenczi, Sandor. *Thalassa: A Theory of Genitality.* New York, 1938.

3 French, Thomas M. *The Integration of Behavior,* Vol. I and II. Chicago, 1952, 1954.

4   Freud, Sigmund. *Three Contributions to the Theory of Sex.*
     New York, 1930.

5   ———. "The Economic Problem in Masochism." *Coll.
     Papers,* Vol. II. London, 1924.

6   ———. "Instincts and Their Vicissitudes." *Coll. Papers,*
     Vol. IV. London, 1946.

7   Gerard, R. W. *Unresting Cells.* New York, 1940.

8   Waelder, Robert. "The Psychoanalytic Theory of Play."
     Psychoanalytic Quarterly, Vol. II, 1933.

9   Sachs, Hanns. "Zur Genese der Perversionen." *Interna-
     tionale Zeitschrift für Psychoanalyse,* Vol. IX, 1923.

Perversions and Genitality

MICHAEL BALINT

Most papers on perversions, after warning the reader of all the difficulties to be encountered, start with a definition of what is perversion and what is not. There have been three types of such definitions, all of them repeated many times in the literature. Unfortunately, all three of them, though serious attempts, are somewhat inexact and thus misleading.

The first type might be called biological. It uses the propagation of the species to differentiate between normal intercourse and perversions. According to all definitions of this kind, masturbation and intercourse using contraceptives belong to the perversions. This is obviously incorrect; neither masturbation nor coitus reservatus is a perversion although, very rarely, either of them may be an unimportant symptom of a complicated structure of perversion.

The second type of definition, going back to Freud and his *Three Essays*, emphasizes the survival of infantile forms of sexual gratification in an adult. This has been a very fruitful idea; it is based on the theory of component instincts and the various organizations of the libido. Unfortunately, this definition excludes from the perversions many forms of homosexuality on the one hand and of the sado-masochistic group on the other which (especially the first) are definitely not survivals of infantile forms of sexuality but later developments.

The third class of definition is based on the theory of object relations. It tries to explain the differences between genitality and the perversions by pointing out the lack of proper love for a human object or the presence of immature forms of love in perversions. Anybody who has had any experience with homosexuals knows that, in them, we may find practically the whole scale of love and hatred that is exemplified in heterosexuality.

To get some brief idea of what we have to deal with, let us start by classifying the perversions, following Freud's example in the *Three Essays*. The first group is that of the different kinds of homosexuality. As I just mentioned, it is a very rich and varied field. This is especially true of the various forms of relationships between the two lovers, irrespective of whether they are men or women. It is fair to say that all the beautiful, all the hideous, all the altruistically loving and all the egotistically exploiting features of heterosexual love can be found in homosexual love as well. There is also the same bliss, the same hatred, the same jealousies, the same unhappy yearning, etc., etc.

The second group of perversions consists of the much less well-studied and documented forms of sadism and masochism. This may seem a bold statement; the literature of the last thirty years or so contains numerous articles, allusions and even books on this topic. Unfortunately, the published material amounts to very little if one discounts the eternal controversy between primary and non-primary sadism and masochism. The paucity of first-hand clinical observations in overtly sadistic or masochistic perverts is truly surprising.

The third group of perversions is the one which is aptly described by the second type of definition quoted above. They seem really to be centered upon a surviving component instinct; to this group belong exhibitionism, voyeurism, the use of other parts of the body instead of the genital zone, etc.

The fourth group consists of a very intriguing conglomeration composed of fetishism, transvestitism and, perhaps, kleptomania. All of these are characterized by the turning away from a living human object and its replacement by something inanimate.

There remain two more groups which I am not certain should be called perversions. One of these groups consists of the activities known as bestialism. According to my experience, admittedly a limited one, this never reaches the height of a proper perversion; it always seems to come about "for want of something better." The unhappy people who indulge in it are either simpletons—sometimes even imbeciles—or they are in the throes of the great passions of puberty without the hope of finding a proper partner. As I see it, these people temporarily make use of the fact that certain animals are in their care by resorting to them as an outlet.

Nor do I think that the remaining forms—necrophilia or the use of immature children as partners—should be classified among the perversions. In my opinion, they belong more properly to the psychoses.

So let us start with the forms belonging to groups two to four. Here we shall perhaps meet fewer complications. After having cleared the field, we may see whether our ideas are of any use in understanding the remaining groups.

In these three groups, it looks as if our second type of definition would be able to account for the facts observed. The sexual life of these people seems to be wrongly organized; instead of genitality being the center, some other component instinct of sexuality appears to have succeeded in usurping the leading role. But is this impression really correct?

Clinical observation of these people shows that satisfaction of the relevant component instinct creates only a state of very high excitement. Although this is definitely pleasurable in itself, it hardly ever leads to a final gratification. The perverse act—e.g., exhibitionism—may be repeated several times in the same bout, each new act producing a further increase of excitement, but the relief, the gratifying end-pleasure, is almost always brought about by genital satisfaction, either in the form of masturbation or, rarely, of some sort of coitus.

The general trend in these perverted activities, therefore, is the same as in normal genitality. There, too, fore-pleasure mechanisms are widely used to raise the tension, to heighten the excitement. All *artes amandi* of world literature contains prescriptions for achieving this increase of excitement by fore-pleasure mechanism, and nothing else. The more one is able to use these mechanisms—to vary them or to invent new forms or combinations—the more expert one is in the art of love.

Now all these practices in love-making have been called "perverted" at various times; they are discouraged, and even threatened with punishment, in a number of strict ethical or religious systems in the same way as perversions are. The similarity, often the practical identity, of the way in which certain civilizations treat perversions, on the one hand, and the subtleties of the art of love, on the other, is really striking.

Not only civilizations, psychology, too, has great difficulty, where borderline cases are concerned, in distinguishing with confidence what is still part of normal sexuality, what is perverse and what is neurotic or psychotic. I have mentioned already that, in my opinion, neither bestiality nor necrophilia nor the sexual use of immature children should be counted among the perversions. But what about the various conditions many people impose before considering anybody as a potential partner? Quoting G. B. Shaw rather freely: "Falling in love means overemphasizing the slight differences between one woman and another." How far is this restriction of freedom of choice of love object—and of gratification—healthy, perverse or neurotic? For instance, is it normal or not to demand that the love object must be tall or petite, fair or dark, very bright or rather simple, domineering or submissive, and so on? Perhaps we may accept the conditions just quoted as normal; when they exact (I cite from my own practice) that a woman limp or even have a false leg, or that the man wear spectacles, or that the woman wear black underwear during coitus, the difficulty of drawing the boundary becomes greater.

I wish to quote here one of Abraham's favorite examples— where the woman, during coitus, had to bid for the bed in which the couple was lying, as at an auction. The bids had to get higher as the excitement increased. The final gratification was the greater the higher the last bid. But all the bids had to be absolutely realistic. She was not allowed to bid fantastic sums; that would have destroyed all the pleasure. . . . In one of my own cases, the bargaining was concerned with what sum the husband ought to pay his wife for her services during coitus. The higher the gratification for the husband, the higher the excitement for the wife, the higher was the agreed fee. Here, too, the same condition prevailed; no exorbitant fees were tolerated. If anything went wrong in this bargaining, the coitus was absolutely unsatisfactory for the man who was my patient. The theoretically important question arises: are these clinical pictures perversions, or neurotic symptoms, or are they still within the limits of the normal?

This may seem an idle question, but its importance becomes immediately apparent when one realizes, as I pointed out above, that in practically all perversions, however abstruse they may appear, the final gratification is brought about by some form of genital action. In other words: fore-pleasure mechanisms are used—both in normal cases and in perverts—to create a high though pleasurable excitement which is finally satisfied through the genitals. This is a clinical fact hardly ever mentioned but of signal importance. It means that all perverse activities, especially the most impressive ones belonging to my classes two, three and four—that is, sadism and masochism, those centered upon one or the other component instincts and the group characterized by fetishism—are only deceptive measures, designed to convince the whole world and the pervert himself that his main concern is the satisfaction of one of the component instincts and that his eventual genital end-pleasure need not be taken seriously. These clinical findings, expressed in analytical terminology, lead us to the castration complex and to its denial, both of them, of course, mentioned numerous times in the psychoanalytic literature on perversions.

All this is well known, but somehow, in our theoretical considerations, we have fallen for the deceptive technique of the pervert and believed, so to speak, that his exhibitionism, cunnilingus or sadism was an end in itself, and not merely a roundabout way to get genital satisfaction in disguise. That means that, in order to escape from the throes of their castration fears, perverts have to pretend *not* to be interested in genital pleasure. As overt castration fear is more frequent in men, this finding may explain why these three groups of perversions are so much more frequent among them.*

Another interesting effect created by this shifting of emphasis and denial is the impression or even the claim that truly perverse

* On the whole, perversions constitute a predominantly male sphere; some forms—like genital exhibitionism—are apparently exclusively male. Two other spheres, where the same male predominance obtains, are criminality and addiction, especially alcoholism. These three fields thus offer a promising starting point for a systematic study of the specific psychology of women.

action is more pleasurable, more exciting than normal coitus.
As the castration fear is present to a certain degree in all of
us, it is not too easy to expose this deceptive pretense. On the
other hand, it is mercilessly unmasked in the old joke about
the bet between a roué and a young man, each of whom brags
that he knows more forms of sexual gratification than the
other. The young man starts by mentioning normal coitus,
whereupon the other accepts his defeat; that one he really did
not think of. Very well—but what about the rest? Why is the
genital form of sexual gratification so much more satisfactory
that it outweighs all the others taken together?

The answer is *not* because it is loosely connected with the
propagation of the species. We need only mention the fairly
satisfactory sexual life of sterile men and women, or of those
using contraceptives. So we have to look for other reasons. It is
true that, in some way, both the whole body and every part of it
are capable of pleasurable sensations. That is, erotic excitement
and erotic pleasure are as widespread, as old as life. But, as I
tried to show as long ago as 1930, this general eroticism is un-
specific, unorganized, and, as yet, not bisexually differentiated;
consequently, it cannot explain the unique importance of
genital sexuality which is always highly organized and, above
all, bisexual.*

The only train of thought that enables us to understand the
special importance of bisexual genitality was originated by
Ferenczi.† According to him, the phylogenetic catastrophe that
compelled our ancestors to give up the easier ways of thalassal
life for the much stricter conditions on dry land, and the onto-

---

* For further details of this and other ideas in this paper *cf.* my book
Primary Love, Hogarth Press, London, 1952, especially chapters 1, 4, 5,
7 and 8.
    † S. Ferenczi: *Thalassa. A Theory of Genitality*, 1924. English trans-
lation, 1938.

genetic catastrophe that compels each one of us to exchange the easier intra-uterine form of existence for one in which we must fend for ourselves, create very strong regressive longings for the return to these early and more pleasurable conditions.

All forms of sexual activity, auto-erotic as well as allo-erotic, can be regarded as more or less successful attempts to achieve this regressive aim. On the whole, their ability to produce orgasm and to provide real satisfaction—i.e., one that is followed by contentment and the feeling of tranquil well-being so characteristic after a gratifying coitus—depends on how near they come to this all-important regression.

The male comes nearest to achieving this regression during coitus: with his semen in reality, with his penis symbolically, with his whole self in phantasy. The woman's role in coitus is more complex. On the one hand, she identifies herself with the male, by surrendering at least temporarily all her masculinity to her partner; on the other, she accepts the role of the all-embracing sea or, in ontogenetic terms, of the mother receiving back her son into her womb.

The willingness to abandon oneself to a highly intense regressive tendency presupposes a fairly well-integrated ego, one which has attained and is able to maintain a good mastery over the various forms of anxiety, especially of castration anxiety. Conversely, this theory explains why we find in practically all perverts—i.e., people who systematically avoid this periodic regression—weakening of the ego, lack of integration, faulty mastery over anxieties, especially over castration anxiety, faulty sense of reality, etc., in the same way as we find them in neurotics.

This train of thought also explains why homosexuality has to be classed among the perversions. Admittedly, one quite often finds in homosexuals an object-love as rich and as diversified as among heterosexuals; one also finds, however, the atmosphere of overpretense and denial that is so characteristic of the other groups of perversions. Homosexuals, too, have to assert that their way of life and of sexual pleasure is more beautiful, more gratifying, more everything than that of normal people. The reason is near at hand. They have to use overemphasis in order to deny—what they all know—that, without normal intercourse, there is no real contentment.

There remains one more group of perversions—a most intriguing one—that consisting of fetishism, transvestitism and, almost certainly, kleptomania. What I said before, namely, that the end-pleasure is brought about only by genital gratification, is well demonstrated by this group. The perverse act brings about only a very high excitement which, in the end, is relieved mostly by masturbation, rarely by some form of coitus. This is evident in fetishism and transvestitism and is very often true of kleptomania as well.

The intriguing problem here is the substitution of the human partner by some inanimate thing. Since psychoanalysis turned away, more or less, from biology and the study of the component instincts and concentrated its interest on objects and our relation to them, fetishism became the fashionable topic in the literature on perversions. This trend was started, in 1927, by Freud himself, who pointed out that, possibly, the fetish should be regarded as a kind of cover memory, i.e., the last object perceived immediately before the final discovery of the castrated female genital. Others followed, showing the anal nature of fetishes—they must be used objects (or the exact opposite: absolutely new), they must have a smell, their undisturbed possession is very reassuring, etc. Again, others demonstrated the processes of splitting, both with regard to the object—the fetish being one of the split-off parts—and with regard to one's own mind. I added to it the fact that most fetishes are hollow; in these cases, the perverse act consists of putting the fetish on or sticking one part of the body—foot, finger, penis, nose, etc., —into it.

All these and certainly still many more interpretations of the function of the fetish are true—in the sense of overdetermination. The fetish is the result of a split, it is a symbolic substitute for the penis, it has anal implications, represents an acceptable alternative for the vagina, can be detached or stolen from its rightful owner, its possession can be enjoyed undisturbed, etc. In fact, one can do with it practically everything one wants to —a very important difference from any human object.

As described first in my paper, *On Genital Love* (1947),* whatever the desired gratification may be, if it is to come from a human object, that object must first be transformed into a cooperative partner. The more primitive, more infantile the instinct, the smaller the degree of cooperation needed. Thus, there is hardly any in voyeurism or exhibitionism, somewhat more in anal bullying. Genital love demands the highest degree of cooperation. In this case, it must amount to a "genital" identification—much more stringent than the usually mentioned "oral" identification—which can be maintained only by a constant testing of reality. By this I mean that a constant watch must be kept on what our partner expects from us and on what we actually satisfy of these expectations. A harmonious relationship can be maintained only if these two are not too far from each other. If they differ widely, effort—often considerable effort—is needed to restore equilibrium. I called this constant watch and effort the "work of conquest," which must go on unceasingly as long as the relationship is to last.

Here is the other important difference between genitality and

* Reprinted in *Primary Love.*

perversion. Perversions do not presuppose a high degree of "genital" identification, they can often do with less, even with much less. Fetishists have gone perhaps the farthest on this road. Once they have acquired a fetish, it is theirs; it does not change; unlike the unpredictable, treacherous human being, it remains forever the same. The fetishist does not have to maintain mutual genital identification by the unceasing work of conquest. The fetish has no wishes, demands, interests of its own; it can be taken for granted.

This kind of relation—a partnership in which only one partner may have desires, wishes, interests and in which the other partner can always be relied upon to be in harmony with the desires and interests of the first—is that of primary love. No need for testing of reality, no need for enduring tensions, no need for any "work of conquest." Our partner is there when and how we want him. Other perverts approach this infantile state by making use of one of their component instincts which demands only as much "work of conquest" as they can tolerate. The fetishist resorts to the use of inanimate objects in his escape. The object of his choice, of course, must show up the ways and means of his escape, of his regression, by being a penis substitute, by demonstrating anal qualities, by representing a substitute womb, etc.

To sum up: perversions are attempts to escape from the two main demands of mature genitality: (1) accepting as real the intense need in ourselves for periodic regressions in the form of heterosexual coitus, and (2) accepting the necessity of the work of conquest, i.e., changing an indifferent object into a cooperative genital partner.

Perverts have to avoid these two tasks, as their ego is not strong enough to stand up to the strains involved; in other words, it is not well enough integrated, it has not achieved a sufficient mastery over the various forms of anxiety, especially castration anxiety. In their search for a possible outlet, they often resort to one of the more primitive, simpler, component instincts and then pretend that the gratification of that instinct is all-important, and that, for them, genital satisfaction is only a by-product. That is, they use idealization on the one hand and denial on the other to cover their steps, thus deceiving both the world and themselves.

The other way for them is to dispense, more or less, with the cooperation of their partner; if they make fewer demands, the partner cannot claim much either and the "work of conquest" exacts much less effort and strain. In this direction, the true fetishist achieves most; he has no need for any human being at all.

The Structure and Aetiology of Sexual Perversion

WILLIAM H. GILLESPIE

A rigid definition of the term "sexual perversion" is probably best avoided, but I hope it will be agreed that it should imply persistent or habitual sexual behavior of a certain type rather than mere isolated acts; that the behavior should be accompanied by specifically sexual excitement; and that it should deviate from some standard of normal sexual conduct. Difficulties arise, however, when we proceed to any attempt to specify this standard of normality. Can there be any universal standard or should we think only in terms of a particular culture at a particular time? If the latter, are we to rely on a statistically defined standard of normality or on the moral code professed by the culture, which may deviate widely from the average actual behavior of its members? Endless difficulties arise, which cannot be discussed here.

I wish to suggest that, despite its manifest limitations, a biological standard has some real advantages. Inasmuch as the sexual instinct has the biological function of ensuring procreation and thus promoting survival of the species, it seems reasonable to designate as a perversion any way of sexual life which interferes seriously with the procreative function. The diagnosis of sexual perversion would then be based on the degree and exclusiveness of the sexual activity, not just on its quality. Such a concept of perversion has a universal validity, unlike the others. Nevertheless, I do not claim for it any status higher than that of a rough yardstick, for it ignores an essential aspect of human sexual life, namely, the psychological relation to the sexual object; it gives no weight to the ego's part in sexual life, normal or perverse, and evades the issue of love and the possibility that an essential element in perversion may be the failure to form a satisfactory loving relationship with a sexual object. However, since perversion shares these features with neurosis and psychosis, the biological concept may provide a valuable method of rough differentiation.

It must be assumed that every reader of this book is thoroughly familiar with Freud's original and classical contribution to the subject in *Three Essays on the Theory of Sexuality* (1905). I will merely state the essence of his concept at that time, namely, that perversion represents the persistence into adult life of elements of infantile ("polymorph-perverse") sexual activity at the expense of adult genitality, these infantile elements having failed to undergo the normal transformations of puberty and having failed also to succumb to the defense mechanisms that would have converted them into neurotic symptoms. Thus Freud arrived at the famous formulation that "neuroses are, so to say, the negative of perversions," and perversion is represented as the mere persistence of the infantile, a kind of atavism of ontogenesis.

This concept of the nature of perversion is a good example of Freud's genius for grasping the connections between things which are not obviously related, in this case perversion, neurosis, and infantile sexuality. It is essential, however, to remember that Freud had already reached this point in his thinking by 1905 and that it was by no means his last word on the subject of perversion. His later work quite clearly implies a much less simple view, as is evident from his papers on homosexuality, sado-masochism, fetishism and other related topics. These later developments in Freud's theory of perversion have been obscured by the fact that, although subsequent editions of the *Three Essays* contain numerous additions and some corrections, Freud left the main text essentially unaltered for the purpose of historical documentation. This has had one unfortunate consequence: less well-informed critics have been led to infer that his early views underwent no further development. I hope to show how far this inference is from the truth.

In his paper on Leonardo, written in 1910, Freud speaks of a fetish as constituting a substitute for the sorely missed penis of the woman; in the same paper, he describes a type of male homosexuality due to repression of attachment to the mother, followed by identification with her and object choice on a narcissistic basis; such homosexuals are running away from other women who might make them unfaithful to their mothers. These points of view show clearly that, by 1910, Freud had already recognized the *defensive* function of certain perversions.

The decisive change came with the paper, A *Child Is Being Beaten* (1919). Here Freud unequivocally relates a particular perverse phantasy to the Oedipus complex and to various forms of defense against it. Moreover, in his discussion he extends these ideas to perversion in general. All later psychoanalytic work on the perversions has been greatly influenced by this paper. Since its publication, perversion has been regarded in analytic writings as a complex psychic formation, expressing defense as well as impulse, and related to the same nuclear

complex as neurosis; it is no longer just the raw material out
of which a neurosis might have been made.

This new way of looking at sexual perversion was carefully
worked out from the theoretical point of view by Sachs in his
paper, *Zur Genese der Perversionen* (1923). He picked out, as
the most important problem about perversion, its relation to
the Oedipus complex, to the unconscious and to repression.
Freud had shown, in *A Child Is Being Beaten*, that the component instinct does not continue in a straight line to perversion
but must first go through the Oedipus complex as a light ray
is refracted by a lens. This is consistent with the fact that
perverse gratification is regularly bound to quite narrow conditions which far exceed the demands of a simple component
instinct. Moreover, pregenital component instincts only excep-
tionally appear in the perversion in an objectless or auto-erotic
form; mostly, they appear after an elaboration which has raised
them to a higher level and made them capable of normal
libidinal cathexis of an object, sometimes of the most refined
kind. Freud's statement that neurosis is the negative of perversion does not exhaust the subject, for it is clear that perversion
is only the conscious part of a much larger *unconscious* system.
In neurosis, the repressed phantasy breaks through only as an
ego-dystonic symptom, whereas, in perversion, it remains capable
of consciousness, being ego-syntonic and pleasurable; apart from
this difference, there is much similarity between the two: both
are mere residues of the great developmental process of infantile
sexuality, the conscious representations of unconscious instincts. Indeed, in some cases, there is an alternation between
neurotic phobia and perverse gratification. Sachs observed such
a change in the course of an analysis, a phobia of beating giving
way to sado-masochistic masturbation phantasies. (I have myself observed two cases where whipping phantasies or practices

were combined with an intense snake phobia.) Drug addiction seems to be intermediate between perversion and neurosis, being clearly a gratification, yet having ostensibly nothing to do with infantile sexuality. (The relation between perversion and drug addiction was later, in 1932, worked out more fully by Edward Glover.)

Just as in the beating phantasies discussed by Freud, only one constant element persists throughout, namely, the idea of being beaten, so in other perversions one element remains constant; it is seen with particular clarity in fetishism, where one bit of a repressed complex remains conscious, like a harmless screen memory which hides the essential piece of infantile sexuality. Thus a perversion comes into being through the preservation in consciousness of a specially suitable piece of infantile experience onto which the infantile pleasure is displaced. This piece of experience must have some peculiar relationship to the ego which allows it to escape repression. Sachs suggests that, when there is a conflict involving a specially strongly developed component instinct, complete victory may be impossible for the ego and repression may be only partially successful; the ego then has to be content with the compromise of repressing the greater part at the expense of sanctioning and taking into itself the smaller part. This solution by division, whereby one piece of infantile sexuality enters the service of repression and so carries over pregenital pleasure into the ego while the rest undergoes repression, *seems to be the mechanism of perversion.*. (It should be noted that the idea of "partial repression" had long ago been anticipated by Abraham (1910), following a suggestion of Freud's.) That this mechanism is used especially to deal with the task of repressing the Oedipus complex is well illustrated in A *Child Is Being Beaten*. Sachs shows that his hypothesis fits equally well the case of male homosexuality based on too strong fixation to the mother, resolution being achieved only by sanction of fixation to the man's own sex, this being incorporated in the ego. Summing up his argument, Sachs emphasises that what he has described is only the mechanism, not the dynamics, of the instinctual victory. The component instinct owes its strength not to the alliance with the ego but to factors of constitution or experience which have caused it to develop more than normal strength.

Up to this time, little attention had been paid to the part played in perversion formation by impulses of aggression and hostility. Freud's (1922) paper on *Jealousy, Paranoia and Homosexuality* began to touch on this theme. The paranoiac was described as using his ambivalence as a means of defense against his homosexuality; but Freud also described a new mechanism in certain types of homosexuality whereby early intense jealousy and hostility for rival siblings yield to repression and transformation, so that the rivals become love objects—the reverse process of that in persecutory paranoia. Further important theoretical developments came in Freud's (1924) paper, *The Economic Problem in Masochism*, where he tries to elucidate the problems of masochism and sadism in terms of the concept of the death instinct.

The importance in general psychopathology of aggression and of early anxieties and primitive defenses against them began to be increasingly stressed, particularly in England, by Melanie Klein and those who were influenced by her work. This is reflected in Edward Glover's (1933) paper, *The Relation of Perversion Formation to the Development of Reality Sense*. Stages in the development of reality sense, he says, should not be considered solely in terms of impulse or object but should be related to stages in the mastery of anxiety, in which the roles of libidinal and destructive impulses alternate. He suggests that perversions may form a developmental series reflecting stages in the overcoming of anxiety about the individual's own body or external objects. Certain perversions are the negative of certain psychotic formations. Perversions represent periodic attempts to protect against current introjection and projection anxieties by excessive libidinization. When some form of infantile anxiety is reanimated in adult life, one way of dealing with the crisis is the reinforcement of primitive libidinization systems, and this gives rise to a perversion. "Perversions help to patch over flaws in the development of reality sense."

Another aspect of the part played by aggression is brought out in Nunberg's (1938) paper, *Homosexuality, Magic and Aggression*. He describes a new type of male homosexuality in which aggression is an integral part of the homosexual love; the aim represents a compromise between aggressive and libidinal impulses and consists of the desire to possess strong men and thus become magically strong and potent. The man is then revenged on women for his mother's rejection, thus restoring his narcissism and strengthening his weak ego.

However, *A Child Is Being Beaten* had drawn particular attention to the role of the Oedipus complex in perversion formation; Freud's (1927) paper *Fetishism* reinforced this insight by its heavy emphasis on castration anxiety and the need for defense against the threat implied in the discovery of the missing penis of females. Fenichel, both in his original textbook (1931) and its later English version (1945), consolidated this view of aetiology for the perversions in general, and this led to an impression of monotony which was criticized by Glover (1933). Nevertheless, it has to be recognized that the castration complex seems to provide a satisfactory explanation for the clinical fact of the much greater incidence in males of perversion in general and of fetishism in particular, a fact which other aetiological formulations do little to explain; Fenichel (1934) answered Glover's criticism quite effectively in his paper, *Defense against Anxiety, particularly by Libidinization.*

The whole question of the psychological significance of the penis was evidently due for review and, in particular, the concept of the phallic phase introduced by Freud in 1923, the essence of which is that the absence of a penis means castration. This review took the form of a historic controversy between Freud and Ernest Jones. (See Freud, 1925a, 1931, and Jones, 1927, 1933.) In *The Phallic Phase* (1933), Jones suggests that sexual inversion is, in essence, hostility to the rival parent which has been libidinized by appropriating the organs of the opposite sex, organs that have been made dangerous by sadistic projection. The genital sadism is derived from earlier oral sadism, which may well be the specific root of male as well as of female homosexuality.

Freud's (1925) paper, *Negation,* and Ferenczi's (1926) paper, *The Problem of the Acceptance of Unpleasant Ideas,* give the theoretical background of ego psychology for Freud's later contributions on perversion, which were concerned largely with fetishism. Negation is a mechanism whereby the ego is able to extend its boundaries by accepting what would otherwise remain repressed, with the proviso that it be consciously denied. The mechanism of negation is given a central position in Freud's (1927) discussion of fetishism. Out of castration fear, the boy denies his perception that the female has no penis. Thus retaining his belief in the female phallus, he yet at the same time gives it up, constructing a compromise object, the fetish, which absorbs all the interest formerly belonging to the female phallus, leaving him with an aversion to real female genitals. This dual attitude to unacceptable reality, says Freud, can occur in other non-psychotic conditions apart from perversion.

Freud (1940 and 1941) returned to this theme in his *Outline of Psycho-Analysis,* Chapter 8, and in *Splitting of the Ego in the Defensive Process.* He states that, in psychosis, complete withdrawal from reality rarely if ever occurs; what occurs is a split in the mind, one part being detached from reality; if this part becomes the stronger, the necessary condition for psychosis is present. Such splits can also be found in fetishism and in neuroses. However, Freud goes on to say that we can speak of a split of the ego in fetishists only in cases where they continue to dread castration despite their fetishistic denial of it. Neuroses differ in that one of the contrary attitudes is repressed, so that there is no split in the ego. Freud himself was in some doubt whether this idea of a splitting of the ego was something new or something long known. It is interesting to note that in his (1894) paper, *The Defence Neuro-Psychoses,* he discusses "splitting of consciousness" at some length; of course, this was a very long time before the concepts of the ego and of repression had been worked out.

Melanie Klein's (1946) paper, *Notes on some Schizoid Mechanisms,* inaugurated the discussion of what may be regarded as a related topic, namely splitting of the instinctual object. In my paper (1952) on the perversions, I attempted to combine the two concepts and to bring them into relation with the oral regression which has impressed so many psychoanalytic writers on the perversions. I suggested that strong castration anxiety leads to a partial regression to pregenital levels, thus accounting for the affinity of some perversions to psychosis. A successful perversion evades psychosis by means of a split in the ego, which leaves a relatively normal part capable of coping with external reality while allowing the regressed part to behave in the limited sexual sphere in a psychotic manner. This implies not merely a libidinal regression but also a regression of the ego and of its relations to objects, of the nature of its anxieties and of its means of defense against them. The ego regresses in part to a stage characterized not only by splitting of the ego but also by splitting of the object. The sexual object of the pervert represents the idealized "good" object resulting from this split; the "bad" object is dealt with in other ways, e.g., by denial, omnipotent annihilation, or phobic avoidance.

It may have been noted that little has been said about the superego in perversion, and, in fact, it is only recently that there has been much discussion on this point. If perversion is a regressive result of the Oedipus complex, and if the superego, as classically conceived, is the heir to the same complex, it would be natural to expect a close relationship between them. At the time when Sachs wrote his paper (1923), the concept of the superego was only beginning to emerge. Had he written later, he would no doubt have discussed how the ego is able to reconcile its maneuver of accepting and adopting as part of itself certain pregenital id impulses with its need to live at peace with the superego. It is true that not all perverts are free from feelings of guilt about their sexual activity, but they generally show much less guilt over their preferred piece of infantile sexuality than would a normal or neurotic person. This leads to the question whether we have to deal with a particular type of superego in the pervert, one which condones just that type of sexual activity rather than any other. If so, how is such a superego developed? May it not be the result of a type of parental attitude to sexuality which gives the impression that genital sexuality is the worst sin and certain pregenital activities are relatively harmless? My own clinical experience lends some support to such a view; it was advanced by several speakers at a symposium of the American Psychoanalytic Association, reported by Arlow (1954).

The foregoing makes no pretense of being a comprehensive critical review of psychoanalytic writings on the structure and aetiology of sexual perversion in general, and no attempt has been made in this chapter to deal with the special psychopathology of individual perversions. I have merely picked out a few of the contributions which seem to me typical and illuminating for the general theory. I shall now attempt to sum up briefly the main points which can be regarded as fairly widely accepted at the present time and, so far as possible, to integrate them.

1. The raw materials out of which a perversion is built are derived from the constituent elements of infantile sexuality.

2. While there may be a clinical condition of polymorphus-perverse sexuality based upon a mere persistence into adult life of infantile sexual elements, the usual clinical form of perversion is not of this kind. It is generally specialized in an elaborate way, so that only one or two circumscribed routes are available leading to the achievement of sexual excitation and the discharge of sexual tension.

3. Perversion in this latter sense is a psychic formation which arises as a method of dealing with the Oedipus complex and, in particular, with castration anxiety.

4. The method involves, in the first place, a regression to pregenital levels of instinctual development, both libidinal and aggressive, resulting in an increased sadism. This leads to anxiety and guilt, and the further development of the perversion is an attempt to cope with this anxiety and guilt, that is, to protect both the self and the object. Libidinization of anxiety, guilt and pain is a specially characteristic method of defense in perversion.

5. Perversion cannot be understood merely as a vicissitude

of instinct, as an id phenomenon. The ego is deeply involved. While an essential element in perversion is a libidinal regression, equally essential in determining a perverse outcome rather than a neurosis or a psychosis is the nature of the ego's defensive maneuvers. The ego accepts the perversion and so allows a circumscribed outlet to sexuality. Having given this sop to Cerberus, the ego is then able to ward off the other elements of the Oedipus complex, as well as the predominantly sadistic regressive products of retreat from that complex. The ego achieves this result at the price of a permanent split in itself and a partial denial of reality. A more extensive (psychotic) denial of reality is at the same time avoided.

6. A full understanding of the aetiology of perversion would include not merely an explanation of its structure, how that structure came into being, and what mechanisms are responsible for it, but also an explanation of what determines this particular outcome rather than any other. This is, in general, a task which daunted Freud himself. Perhaps it is enough to say, with Sachs, that the dynamics of the instinctual victory which characterizes perversion must be sought in the strength of the component instincts, and that this strength is derived from inherited constitutional factors combined with infantile experiences which favor the excessive development of such factors. Twin studies have provided some evidence of a hereditary element in homosexuality, while psychoanalytic work has shown how frequently early environmental factors are operative, such as an overseductive mother and a weak or absent father. I doubt if we are yet in a position to explain satisfactorily what determines the outcome of perversion rather than something else. I think it can be said, however, that we now have some understanding of the processes whereby a perversion comes into being.

REFERENCES

Abraham, Karl. "Remarks on the Psychoanalysis of a Case of Foot and Corset Fetishism." *Selected Papers*. London, 1927.

Arlow, Jacob. "Perversion: Theoretical and Therapeutic Aspects" (Panel Report). *Journal of the American Psychoanalytic Association*, Vol. II, 1954.

Bak, Robert. "Fetishism." *Journal of the American Psychoanalytic Association*, Vol. I, 1953.

Fenichel, Otto. *Perversionen, Psychosen, Charakterstörungen*. Vienna, 1931.

——. *The Psychoanalytic Theory of Neurosis*. New York, 1945.

Ferenczi, Sandor. "The Problem of the Acceptance of Unpleasant Ideas." *Further Contributions*. London, 1926.

Freud, Sigmund. "The Defence Neuro-Psychoses" (1894). *Coll. Papers*, Vol. I. London, 1924.

——. *Three Essays on the Theory of Sexuality* (1905). London, 1949.

——. *Leonardo da Vinci* (1910). New York, 1916.

——. "A Child Is Being Beaten" (1919). *Coll. Papers*, Vol. II. London, 1924.

——. "Certain Neurotic Mechanisms in Jealousy, Paranoia and Homosexuality" (1922). *Coll. Papers*, Vol. II. London, 1924.

——. "The Infantile Genital Organization of the Libido" (1923). *Coll. Papers*, Vol. II. London, 1924.

——. "The Economic Problem in Masochism" (1924). *Coll. Papers*, Vol. II. London, 1924.

——. "Some Psychological Consequences of the Anatomical Distinction between the Sexes" (1925). *Coll. Papers*, Vol. V. London, 1950.

——. "Negation" (1925). *Coll. Papers*, Vol. V. London, 1950.

———. "Fetishism" (1927). *Coll. Papers,* Vol. V. London, 1950.

———. "Female Sexuality" (1931). *Coll. Papers,* Vol. V. London, 1950.

———. "An Outline of Psycho-Analysis" (1940). *International Journal of Psychoanalysis,* Vol. XXI, 1940.

———. "Splitting of the Ego in the Defensive Process" (1941). *Coll. Papers,* Vol. V. London, 1950.

Gillespie, W. H. "Notes on the Analysis of the Sexual Perversions." *International Journal of Psychoanalysis,* Vol. XXXIII, 1952.

Glover, Edward. "On the Aetiology of Drug Addiction." *International Journal of Psychoanalysis,* Vol. XIII, 1932.

———. "The Relation of Perversion Formation to the Development of the Reality Sense." *International Journal of Psychoanalysis,* Vol. XIV, 1933.

Jones, Ernest. "The Early Development of Female Sexuality." *International Journal of Psychoanalysis,* Vol. VIII, 1927.

———. "The Phallic Phase." *International Journal of Psychoanalysis,* Vol. XIV, 1933.

Klein, Melanie. "Notes on Some Schizoid Mechanisms." *International Journal of Psychoanalysis,* Vol. XXVII, 1946.

Nunberg, Hermann. "Homosexuality, Magic and Aggression." *International Journal of Psychoanalysis,* Vol. XIX, 1938.

Payne, Sylvia. "Some Observations on the Ego Development of the Fetishist." *International Journal of Psychoanalysis,* Vol. XX, 1939.

Sachs, Hanns. "Zur Genese der Perversionen." *International Zeitschrift für Psychoanalyse,* Vol. IX, 1923.

Elimination of Guilt
as a Function of Perversions

RITSKE LE COULTRE

After studying a number of different perversions, it became evident to me that it is necessary to distinguish clearly between the real guilt feelings attached to the repressed conflict in these cases—feelings which are actually eliminated by the perversion—and the social fears which lie on the surface and are often interpreted as guilt feelings, but which are capable of being removed by fairly simple measures. In the analysis of a number of cases, I was able to observe this lack of real guilt feeling and the way in which it had arisen.

Case I

An unmarried woman consulted me because of hysterical depressions, anxieties, fleeting symptoms of conversion, and sexual anaesthesia. On closer examination, the anxieties proved to be states of depersonalization. I shall not go into the case as a whole but shall confine myself to drawing attention to a peculiarity of the phantasies in which she indulged while masturbating. In these, a girl was forcibly subjected to coitus by a rough, very masculine man, being compelled to lie in a knee-elbow position. It was thus coitus *a tergo*, a position that seemed bestial to the patient and was never used by her in coitus with her lover. A special circumstance was that sometimes the girl in this phantasy was held by another, so that she had to submit defenselessly to the act of violence. There were some variations on this theme, one of which struck me because of the repression of its sexual character. In this, a girl was sent upstairs to be punished. She had to lie face downwards on her bed, propped on her elbows and with bare buttocks, and her little brother had to go with her to see that these instructions were properly carried out. Later, the father was to come to beat the child. The fact that, in this second phantasy, the sexual content of coitus was changed into punishment becomes intelligible if we note that the protagonist is the father. It is clear that things are complicated here by anal exhibitionism.

During her analysis, the patient masturbated with increasing frequency. Initially, masturbation did not play a very important part, but the need of this solace became greater and greater and the patient took to going to bed in the daytime to masturbate. The act was always accompanied by the phantasies mentioned and, in these, the patient identified herself completely with the male role. Masturbation was usually preceded by restlessness and a sort of aggressive mood, both of which afterwards completely disappeared; the patient then felt herself to be a sweet, good girl, soothed and well behaved.

It had become evident to me, from the patient's dreams and from other things, that her masturbation was charged with unconscious guilt. In short, I could not help feeling surprised at the result of this form of masturbation, from which she emerged refreshed and as if reborn.

Her analysis made no progress during this period; her associations turned on her masculine aggressive feelings. Then she masturbated again and was a good, well-behaved girl once more. Simultaneously, she produced two phenomena which to my mind had something to do with the effect of masturbation, namely, an enormous logorrhoea and diarrhea. After defecation, the patient had the feeling of having got rid of everything in herself that was impure and dirty (the feeling of being dirty was repugnant to her), and it soon became clear to her that her logorrhoea had the same significance. Having spat out the dirty matter in my presence, she was able to feel clean again. It could be described as a kind of autotomy, a symbolical ejection of what was not acceptable to the ego. What she said was not digested but was thrown in my face, as if to say: "There you are, there's all the dirt for you, sort it out for yourself." Thus I received the impression that the masturbation and the phantasies attending it were based on the same principle; we were involved in an endless process, a phenomenon that was always enacted in the same way. I realized that the masturbation phantasy served as a perversion, keeping away a forbidden idea, and decided to suggest to my patient that she should give up masturbation for a while as an experiment to see what would happen. The first reaction was a reproduction of the rage she had experienced as a child in consequence of the maternal prohibition of masturbation. Subsequently, however, it came to light that the patient was tormented by sadistic masculine phantasies, of which she could now no longer get rid in her accustomed fashion. Once or twice, the resulting inner discomfort became more than she could bear, with the result that she reverted to masturbation.

Before long, however, a remarkable change took place. First of all, side by side with the masculine sadistic phantasies, feminine feelings directed toward me made their appearance, with the result that the patient herself came to be aware that the abandonment of masturbation was resulting in transference feelings coming more distinctly to the fore. Suddenly, however, she started masturbating to the accompaniment of a pronounced masochistic phantasy. In this, she was herself the woman who was taken forcibly, again in the accustomed knee-elbow position. The orgasm was intense. This act of masturbation left a severe moral hangover; the patient felt depressed and full of guilt. Her phantasy followed the formula: "I am forcibly subjected to coitus by a man (analyst-father)" and the reaction showed clearly that these desires were attended by deep guilt feelings.

The abandonment of masturbation had yet other effects. For the first time, a vaginal sensation, to wit a hungry feeling, made its appearance; and, simultaneously with the emergence of these feminine feelings, the body-ego feeling changed. It had previously been greatly disturbed in the case of this patient; she hardly experienced herself bodily, the sense of weight did not exist, and she often had the sensation of floating instead of walking. Now, however, she began to feel extremely heavy, so heavy that it seemed to her as if she might be going to fall through the couch. Sometimes, she felt she weighed fifteen stone. Eventually, a memory was produced of her sister's being beaten on the buttocks.

This case, in short, is found to be characterized by a central, guilt-laden conflict arising from masochistic desires directed toward the father. It is necessary to escape from this conflict, and a way is found in identification with the principal figure in it, the father. The guiltlessness is the result of identification with the latter and the patient's denial of her own feelings. Gratification of the original desire takes place indirectly by entering into the sensations of the girl in the phantasy. It is important to note that, in many cases, the gratification thus perversely arrived at is not complete but is seriously inhibited. The inhibition of the ego-feeling is also important; in this case, it resulted in chronic depersonalization through the complication of tendencies to anal exhibitionism.

Case II

This was a case of exhibitionism. The patient, a married man of thirty-five, performed frequent acts of exhibitionism which ended by getting him into trouble with the police. The disgrace caused him to accept treatment and to bring it to a successful conclusion.

The patient had a younger brother, who was homosexual or bisexual. At the age of ten, he was seduced by a servant girl; according to what he said, the coitus ran its normal course, ending in orgasm. The girl was subsequently pestered by him and his brother, who was present at the scene, but he ended by developing a strong aversion toward her.

In his fifteenth year, he fell deeply in love with a girl whom he had never been able to forget. An end was put to their innocent relationship by the girl's strict parents, and the girl and he unprotestingly resigned themselves to their enforced separation. In about his eighteenth year, he started exhibiting himself in the street and, occasionally, at home when there were women or girl visitors. His marriage, in which he appeared to be capable of coitus, had been a disappointment. His wife cared little for sexual intercourse and it became more and more difficult for him to accomplish the sexual act.

Exhibiting himself, however, became a daily practice; he sometimes indulged in it from twenty to fifty times a day. Feelings of guilt were totally absent. He knew he was performing a forbidden act but that meant nothing to him; his only fear was of discovery by his family or the police and, when he was discovered, the reaction was most violent. He made an attempt at suicide which nearly succeeded and, if I remember correctly, he subsequently had a fit of hysteria. He had had a similar fit years before when his pocketknife broke in two while he was engaged in doing some minor job.

The exhibitionism did not, of course, cease after his contact with the police, though he made great efforts to control himself. But the urge now came upon him in the most impossible places, e.g., shops, where discovery was inevitable.

The patient had great difficulty in giving an exact description of his state of mind during the exhibitionistic acts. Sometimes, for instance, when he saw a girl approaching in an empty street, he managed to avoid exhibiting himself by hurriedly taking to flight. But, at other times, a point was reached from which there was no going back. He was inwardly in a state of great agitation and he had discovered that he would stare at the girl with abnormally large eyes. In the course of the analysis, he came to understand the meaning of the way in which he looked at the girl; he wanted to see what impression he was making on her. It appeared that fright on her part did not please him overmuch but that it was preferable to the absence of any reaction; in the latter event, he regarded the act of exhibitionism as a failure. The ideal result was that the girl should take a full interest in the act and demonstrate marked sexual excitement. The patient had never had an erection or ejaculation or orgasm during the exhibitionistic act.

At first, I thought this absence of erection and ejaculation abnormal in an exhibitionist. I based my opinion on analytic literature which states that the perversion is characterized by the appearance of orgasm. This, however, is not in agreement with accounts given by non-analytic authors. According to Havelock Ellis, the exhibitionist commonly displays no signs of sexual excitement, his desires being satisfied by the emotional reaction provoked in the woman. Moll and Wulffen do not believe masturbation—which only seldom accompanies the exhibitionistic act—to be essential; Krafft-Ebing describes a case in which there was a half-erection and ejaculation never occurred. A patient of Garnier's, who exhibited himself in churches, said: "I do not go there to procure myself pleasure but for something more serious. I watch the effect on the faces of the ladies to whom I show my organs. I want to see them express a profound joy; I really want them to be forced to say to themselves: 'How impressive nature is, seen thus!' "

To return to my case, we see that it is a little more complicated than the previous case, for here the negative Oedipus complex is the center to which the guilt feelings are tied. The exciting things that must be avoided are the patient's attachment to his father, his feeling himself a girl in relation to him, seeing his father's genitals. The roles are therefore reversed; in the exhibitionistic act, the patient assumes the father role and displays his penis. But, by becoming absorbed in the girl's feelings, he is enabled to experience the original sexual excitement in a modified, guiltless form. (I also found that the denial of castration was present; but the intention to induce the girl to show her penis did not appear to be present.) Moreover, this is another example of the completed cycle. The original experience on seeing the father's genitals is revived in sharing the feelings it is desired to rouse in the girl.

Case III

This was a young man with bisexual tendencies, who took a great interest in young boys, and particularly in their penes.

He was much given to phantasies about young boys and, whenever possible, he would strike up an acquaintance with them at swimming pools and at the seaside. Because of his fear of the police, he hardly ever went further than that, nearly everything being enacted in phantasy; only once or twice had he actually done anything. He used to imagine that he was playing with a boy's penis, causing its erection by rubbing. He would talk to the boy, telling him he would grow into a big man, when he would have a big penis, and that it was a very good thing to play with his penis and to have an erection, and that later he would be allowed to go to bed with women.

Apart from this, he had definite heterosexual tendencies; he was capable of coitus but only if the girl had firm, erect breasts. He dared not marry, knowing that in a short time the woman's breasts were bound to become somewhat flabbier, in which case he would be doomed to impotence. So he had always to seek out young girls, for whom his love never lasted long. As a curious detail, I mention the patient's favorite reading, a book by Frank Thiess, in which a certain scene, which greatly excited him, recurs several times. In this, a woman is standing and looking at herself in the mirror. Her breasts are so young that they tilt upwards a little too much. The nipples are thus a little too high and, to perfect the picture, she presses them down a little. I think that I may omit explanations. In the last resort, the patient's quest was a quest for the penis. It appeared, however, from the analysis of the phantasy, that the young boys with whom he tampered represented the patient himself and that he was given a manual erection by his father, the latter giving him explicit permission to have the erection. But the patient did not play the father-role only; he also played that of the mother. The latter implied not only pre-Oedipal physical care but positive permission to have an erection.

What he really would have liked would have been that his mother, too, should show her penis, which would be much bigger than the patient's, and that she should tell him that he, too, had a beautiful penis, which would grow bigger and bigger.

It is clear in this perverse phantasy: (1) that the Oedipal situation is denied; (2) that woman's lack of a penis is denied; (3) that a reversion to the phallic phase takes place but on the understanding that woman possesses a penis; (4) that the wish-phantasy—in which the parents' loving permission to possess a penis and to derive pleasure from it is granted—does not remain in the consciousness as such because too much guilt is attached to it; it therefore has to be disguised, and the disguise takes the form of an inversion of the *dramatis personae*. In the perverse act or phantasy, the patient assumes the father-and-mother role and finds a way of entering into the boys' feelings, thus closing the circle. In this patient, orgasm was clearly disturbed; erection and ejaculation occurred but libidinal feelings were poor.

Closer investigation into the question of guilt feelings in these and other perversions is certainly warranted. I should, however, like to add one more case to this series. It is of a type with which every analyst is familiar and is certainly not regarded as belonging to the perversions. But, on closer investigation, it reveals strong affinities with the characteristics of perversion which I have mentioned.

The case I have in mind was that of a woman of thirty. She was unmarried but had a relationship with a man that could be put on a par with marriage. She was regularly unfaithful to him with casual acquaintances.

The process of becoming conscious of the positive transference ran a very laborious course because she could not bear the pain of an unrequited love. The well-known reaction occurred: she fled from this situation into acting out. The usual interpretation of acting out is that it is an expression, in actions outside the analysis, of what is trying to force its way up into consciousness in the analysis.

In this case, however, it was evident that the acting out had an entirely different significance. Two distinct forces were at work. The patient's transference feelings were genuinely feminine, based on her infantile attitude to her father; they filled her whole being and were linked with all her ideals and deeper emotions. What she felt in her adventures with casual lovers constituted a defense against these deeper emotions and an escape into masculinity. On the physical plane, sexual gratification was the result of titillation of the clitoris; on the mental plane, gratification was achieved by entering into the feelings of the man. Furthermore, the sexual play meant to her simultaneously castration of the man and an appropriation of his penis. Afterwards, she had a tremendous feeling of triumph. On the other hand, the experience of being a woman was connected with feelings of guilt and inferiority.

She did not become affectively attached to the men with whom she copulated. Subjectively, she felt that the act did not touch her mentally and guilt feelings never arose. The sexual feelings which were nevertheless present ran their course, as it were, at the periphery of her personality. The original position, Oedipal love for the father, had been abandoned; she identified herself with the father and chose the masculine role. The forbidden desire was to be a man and to love a woman. This desire was denied. The patient next identified herself with a woman (mother) in phantasy, thus being a would-be woman, vicariously experiencing male orgasm in coitus. Her own orgasm was weak. (In similar cases, the male orgasm is sufficient in itself to bring about orgasm in the woman.) The paradoxical aspect of the situation is that a woman should identify herself with a woman. What makes this identification so striking is that it was preceded by another, *i.e.*, with the father. Thus we have a parallel with exhibitionism, in which the negative Oedipus complex also proves to be the starting point.

This form of sexuality can thus be said to be characterized by:

1. Lack of attachment to a definite object.

2. Detachment from the sexual functions of the rest of the personality, accompanied by an absence of guilt feelings and inner conflict; rather, when a reaction in the latter direction could be demonstrated, it did not take the form of a conflict between ego and superego, but of a real fear of condemnation or punishment; *i.e.*, it resembled the forerunner of the feeling of guilt.

3. An essential in coitus is the maximum possible satisfaction of the partner. Women try to make men copulate as much as possible; men try to call forth a maximal number of gratifications in the women. Sexual excitement in another is in itself reason enough to desire coitus. In this matter, we have to distinguish (*a*) the narcissistic factor: "What a wonderful man I am!", "What an attractive woman I am!" and (*b*) the factor of identification.

4. The fourth characteristic is the well-known fact that this activity is an overcompensation for an opposite tendency: in men, to play a passive homosexual role, and, in women, to play an active masculine role.

5. The final libido is in these cases often poor. I say "often" because it is difficult to define the intensity of a feeling. In cases in which therapeutic results were obtained, patients spontaneously informed me that orgasm was accompanied by

much greater intensity of feeling. The poor quality of the libido results in a kind of insatiability. In men, there is sometimes a certain reserve in regard to orgasm or a tendency to delay it as long as possible.

If we consider the well-known narcissistic form of homosexuality, we find a similar closed circle. The center of the inner life is Oedipal love of the mother, from which an escape is made by identification with her and a narcissistic objectchoice; in sexual activity, there is strong identification with the feelings of the male partner.

Apart from the symptoms of perversion mentioned in analytic literature, I should like to draw attention to the following:

1. The effect of the perversion in eliminating guilt. What strikes us as guilt feeling is social fear, which is easily removed.

2. Identification with the partner in the central inner conflict. This is an escape from the guilt-and-fear-ridden situation. In the actual perverse act, the patient plays the role of the partner in the central conflict but vicariously experiences the feelings of the real object. The circle is closed. The satisfying element is the climax, which, it is true, is impaired. (Identification with the opposite number in the guilt-ridden conflict and vicarious experiencing of the feelings of the actual partner are not distinguished in analytic literature.)

3. Orgasm is impaired, as was pointed out by Freud. It may be added that, in a number of perverse acts, satisfaction is not effected during the act but is achieved in subsequent masturbation.

4. The strong vicarious entering into the feelings of the real partner implies a high valuation put upon any manifesta-

tion of sex. In some cases, one may even speak of provocation of sexual excitement in the partner.

5. The detachment of coitus from the rest of the personality, with "pseudo-genitality."

6. The ego is definitely impaired because the most important central feelings are denied and repressed.

7. Absence of attachment to the object. This characteristic exists to a much lesser extent with the group of perversions by "change of object" described by Freud in his *Three Essays*.

It appears that, in many cases, one evasive move, namely, that of the positive to the negative Oedipus complex, is not sufficient; the second move, described above, is required to bring about the elimination of guilt.

Perversion, Cultural Norm and Normality

WARNER MUENSTERBERGER

The problem of perversion and deviant behavior is not confined to psychology and psychiatry. It also exists in the domains of sociology, anthropology and history. There was a time when any open discussion of sexual matters was taboo. For was not all sexuality looked upon as sin? This attitude has undergone considerable change. Even in recent years and within our own cultural environment, we can observe a decided shift in ideas about decency and sex mores.

Yet, in a few respects, our modern versions seem a little old-fashioned while the ancients appear to have entertained some rather fancy notions. For example, in 1434, the Emperor Siegismund had occasion to visit the town of Berne in Switzerland. Before leaving, he extended his official thanks to the city fathers for having permitted him and his men to make free use of the town's brothel.[1] Visiting dignitaries are accorded no such license today in our part of the world.

Or take this gentle hint from The Ladies Dictionary, published in 1694: "It is not becoming a person of quality, when in the company of ladies, to handle them roughly, to put his hand on their necks, or their bosoms. . . ."[2]

As to the custom of men and women bathing together, today it is accepted as a matter of course in some countries while being forbidden by law or considered highly improper in others.

The social environment we live in is constantly changing and shifting. How far does this affect our ideas about normality or deviant behavior? One need not quote Kinsey to establish the fact that our aims and needs are largely conditioned by culture and social structure.

Is it considered a perversion when a man embraces and kisses another man? Or when a brother and sister perform sexual intercourse? Are they behaving in a perverted manner even though they are simply talking to each other? The answer to these questions is to be found, at least in part, in the relationship between the acts and the cultural environment in which they take place.

When the president of the French Republic embraces and kisses the recipient of a military honor, it is hardly regarded as an act of homosexual intention. Yet, in other cultures, it might be a suspicious sign of asocial tendencies if two men merely touch each other.

Similarly, it has frequently been pointed out that, in certain societies, brother-sister incest belonged to a particular institution within the socio-religious system. In sharp contrast, any sort of physical contact between male and female siblings is met with disgust or even punishment by a number of primitive peoples.

What often seem to be contradictions are actually culture-bound adaptations, rooted in the interaction between physiological, psychological and environmental forces. This is why the traditional behavior pattern is often confused with the concept of normality. Freud alluded to this phenomenon as early as 1908 in his paper on *"Civilized" Sexual Morality and Modern Nervousness.*

A year before, William I. Thomas, a professor of sociology in this country, had written: "It is certainly in virtue of susceptibility to the opinion of others that society works—through public opinion, fashion, tradition, reproof, encouragement, precept and doctrine—to bring the individual under control and make him a member of society; and it is doubtful whether this could have been accomplished if a peculiar attitude of responsiveness to opinion had not arisen in sexual relations, reinforcing the more general and cognitive impressionability."[3]

The point I wish to make here is that much of what has been termed "normality" is actually dependent on what is called normal *in our time* and subject to our particular experience. A few field observations may help to make this clear. To begin with, we find a great number of primitive communities in which overt bestiality, homosexuality, masochism and sadism do not belong in the province of hidden vice. Indeed, they may even be part of a special ceremony or the overall process of growing up, as in the initiation rituals of Australian and South Seas tribes.

There is a rather famous example in the tribe of the Marind-anim in Dutch New Guinea. The initiation ceremony begins with the separation of the boy from his mother and from village activities. Each boy is under the observation and guidance of a man to whom he owes absolute obedience. At night, he has to sleep next to his guardian and submit to him whenever he makes pederastic demands. While each man is described as guarding his particular initiand jealously, at the appearance of a certain ghost called Sosom or *Tepo-anim* ("anus-man"), a homosexual orgy takes place between the men and the novices.[4]

From the field report, it is difficult to arrive at a fuller understanding of the ego development of these people. We do learn
that the men are ready to exchange their wives for labor services
and that festive orgies are occasions for promiscuity.[5] Yet there
is little to explain this sort of institutionalized collective homosexuality. Both sexes, we are told, are segregated throughout
most of their married life—the men together with the novices
in the men's house, the women with their small children of
both sexes and the young unmarried girls in the family huts.

Hence it may be assumed that the early environment of the
little boy, surrounded as he is by women and girls, interferes
with a proper identification with the father. Analogous situations
in clinical psychoanalysis lead us to believe that this *cultural
institution* of divided quarters and an almost completely segregated family life has this pathological effect (pathological from
our point of view) on the entire tribe.

The Keraki, another New Guinea tribe, have related customs.
When the anthropologist Williams first came to stay with them,
the natives tried to conceal the fact that homosexuality was
quite "natural" among them. But once they felt secure enough
to confide in him, they had little reason to hide what was considered as being part of the "norm."

"It is actually regarded as essential to the growing boy," wrote
Williams, "to be sodomized. More than one informant being
asked if he had ever been subjected to unnatural practice
answered, 'Why, yes! Otherwise how should I have grown?' . . .
There is indeed no question as to the universality of the practice.
It is commonly asserted that the early practice of sodomy does
nothing to inhibit a man's natural desires when later on he
marries. . . ."

Among these people, husband and wife live together and,
in contrast to the Marind-anim, both pay attention to their
children. The only other indication of latent homosexual tend-

encies is the temporary exchange of wives as a gesture of personal friendship among the men.[6] (The Marind-anim lend their wives in exchange for labor.)

Among the Central Australian tribe of the Nambutji, Róheim observed a similar kind of institutionalized and ritualized homosexual practice. Here the novices are subincised by their future wife's father, who then uses the young man for some time as his "boy-wife." The novice has to obey him and remain at his disposal whenever he is wanted.[7]

Obviously, the foregoing are examples of bisexuality rather than homosexuality. The passive-anal attitude of the novice is plainly a compromise. To the young Keraki, it is the price he must pay to gain the old man's strength and position and to deal with his aggression. By incorporating the initiator's penis, he can become an initiator himself.

For the Marind-anim, the lack of early identification with the father is overcome by the passive-anal submission of the novice. In other words, through the magic of contagion, he may from then on enjoy his own virility. This masculine identification of the initiator is a significant factor.

As I mentioned previously, the young novices are sometimes called "boy-wives." The "husband," then, is the initiator who subincises or circumcises the boy. Among the Big Nambas, on the Island of Malekula in Melanesia, the young lads are lined up and forbidden to turn their heads. Then their initiators come from behind, "carrying sticks and branches from the nettletree, and each of them in turn belabours all the boys with his stick and rubs the leaves up and down the back of each. The pain which the poor lads have to bear is intense, and often a man will have on his back scars resulting from this ordeal."[8] The following morning, they are taken to the river to be circumcised.

The fusion of homosexual attachment, which these men

defend with curious jealousy, and extremely sadistic procedures would seem to be due to a high amount of ambivalence toward the up-and-coming generation of young competitors. The Nambutji who subincizes his future son-in-law and uses him as his boy-wife is compromising between sadism and incestuous desires for his daughter. In this sense, the pederastic relationship between initiator and initiand is an act of aim-inhibited castration on the part of the initiator. The young man's masochistic submission, however, permits him later to "deprive" his tormentor of his daughter.

For the initiator, it is also some sort of retaliatory measure similar to those observed in the initiation ceremonies of secret societies in our own culture. A Free Mason, talking about such a ceremony, remarked: "What was done to me, I now want to do to him." This man clearly understood his paternal identification.

From studies of many other primitive tribes, it is known that outright homosexual practices do occur occasionally. But it is rather doubtful that they serve as regular sexual activity. Some peoples even consider masturbation unnecessary, since they accept premarital sex relationships. *Collectively* institutionalized homosexuality is reported from comparatively few tribes.

Now and then, we learn of particular situations where homosexuality is part of a functional prerequisite, as among some mountain tribes in Morocco. Here homosexual intercourse with a person who possesses *baraka* (power in the sense of *mana*) is regarded as beneficial. A similar motivation applies where a boy cannot learn the Koran properly unless a teacher uses him for pederastic intercourse.[9]

Much has been said about the reversed sex role of Siberian shamans who live or lived as transvestites. The change included their manner of speech, the way they wore their hair and their general appearance. They would seek sex partners and marry them in a traditional wedding ceremony. The "man" would do the man's work, go hunting and fishing; the "female" partner would stay at home and do the domestic work.

Similarly, among a number of American Indian tribes where sex and social role are typified by standard behavior, a man with homosexual inclinations becomes a *berdache*, wearing a woman's dress, participating in women's life, and even taking a "husband."[10-13]

While societies like these accept transvestitism and homosexuality, they seem to insist on a more or less complete reversal of the social role, demanding behavior adjustment in terms of the other sex. Yet, as has been noted, considering our acquaintance with a great number of primitive peoples, examples of homosexual practices are comparatively rare.

At this point, a distinction should be made between individual and collective perversion. Where individual homosexuality is known and accepted, people will try to find a solution according to the laws and limits set by their environment. The natives of Southern Celebes, for example, speak of male, female and *kawé* (for which the Indonesian translation is "seorang het," meaning "human it"). Here, again, society would provide a specific position for such *kawé*.

A fellow named Taking would stay at home at the women's quarters, participating in men's work only if absolutely unavoidable. His manner of sitting, talking and dressing was practically that of a woman. During rituals, he would sit with the older women of status but would also take part in the work of the women of lower status, as well as in the ritual performances of the women of higher status. Once, when called to court, he appeared in man's attire and was teased a bit by those present.

This man had chosen his role during latency, when he was about seven years old, at a time when, among these people, children start to play different games, according to whether they are boys or girls. No further information is given as to his family, his childhood, or his personal life. When questioned about intercourse per anum, he showed distaste. From other informants it was learned that they indulged in mutual masturbation.[14]

The identification of this man with the women, with their way of life and their work, is evident. One may say he never left the women. When he had to make his decision at the age of seven, he did not abandon his pregenital ties. This was his way of dealing with reality and the demands made on him. He himself, like those around him, accepted his deviation *as deviation*. Except for the open consent of his social environment, his ego response would not seem too different from that of a passive homosexual with transvestite manifestations in our own culture.

However, when it comes to societies where collective homosexual practices are institutionalized and belong to the daily life of the community, we have to think in terms of a different ego structure. Evidently, among the Marind-anim or the Keraki of New Guinea or the Big Nambas of the New Hebrides or the Nambutji in Central Australia, aggressive impulses against the younger generation are fused with sexual ones. The open aggression of the older men against the young novices, who are their future competitors, is a social device.

It may seem to us inconceivable that the young lads are first isolated from their mothers, then frightened by the appearance of ghosts, threatened with death, beaten and circumcised, as well as homosexually abused. But then we may give a thought to how often, in our own society, older children torment younger ones, how older siblings tease and browbeat their little brothers and sisters in order to reassure themselves as to their own omnipotence.

By the same token, the adoption of a "boy-wife" by the older men is a counterphobic act against their own anxieties. Identifying with the young competitor, they dramatize their anxiety and make sexual demands on him. The accompanying rituals—the appearance of masked men representing ghosts, the use of bull roarers for the voices of ghosts, the isolation of the boys from the village life and their harsh treatment— all these fear-arousing dramatizations are counterphobic measures of the older generation. To reassure themselves, the older men let loose at the novices, one of the mechanisms of their aggressive attitude being their sadistic pederastic relationship with them.

In this way, a defensive counterphobic onslaught somehow became a social institution, providing a means of dealing with potential dangers from the new generation. At the same time, the young fellows seem to think that only after going through these passive sexual stages may they take their active social position. Remember the significant answer of the Keraki man: "Otherwise how should I have grown?" Submissiveness appears to be the condition which later on permits him to identify with the aggressor.

We noted previously that these novices as small boys were surrounded almost entirely by women. Conviction that it would take a "father's" strength to master them was in keeping with their ideas regarding masculinity. Only by submitting to the initiator and incorporating his penis could the novice overcome his infantile anxieties. Only then would he gather enough energy to behave like a man, according to his image of a powerful father, and win a woman for himself.

If it is agreed that adult sexual behavior is regulated by society, can one say the ambivalent attitude toward the young generation among these tribes is "normal" within the limits of the cultural habitat? This perverted behavior is a form of conduct belonging to the cultural norm. In other words, it is an attitude toward sexuality that is fully accepted or even demanded by the particular culture, yet is incompatible with Western codes of "normal" behavior. Nevertheless, these communities function. Their members are adequate, competent people operating according to the needs, conditions, laws and common goals of their society.

As Erikson once said, "They cannot afford to create a community of wild eccentrics, of infantile characters, or of neurotics."[15] In short, the theme of human relationships, which in societies like ours is dealt with intrapsychically, is elaborately dramatized in these primitive cultures, being part of the very rhythm and ritual of their way of life.

Viewed in this light, can we regard their perversions as abnormalities? A novice who reacted "normally," according to our ideas, by not complying would be a deviant among these tribes. Revolting against elementary forms of their code of behavior, he would not be shouldering his responsibilities and would thus throw his future life off balance.

It would seem that traditional growth patterns and social conditions may run counter to our notions regarding normality. In other words, the norm and our ideas about bio-psychologically defined normality do not necessarily coincide. What, then, is bio-psychological normality? The genetic orientation in psychoanalytic theory offers an objective yardstick.

In Jones's opinion, "the nearest attainable criterion of normality is fearlessness."[16] Freud thought it was "impossible to define health except in terms of metapsychology, i.e., of the dynamic relations between those agencies of the psychical apparatus, the existence of which psychoanalysis has discovered. . . ."[17]

Recently, Kubie stated: "Whether or not a behavioral event is free to change depends not upon the quality of the act itself, but upon the nature of the constellation of forces that has produced it. No moment of behavior can be looked upon as neurotic unless the processes that have set it in motion predetermine its automatic repetition irrespective of the situation, the utility, or the consequences of the act."[18]

In view of the ever-present "constellation of forces" it is difficult to determine what is strictly pathological behavior. Many potentialities are molded by the cultural environment. We assume that our biological inheritance contains elements which decide certain behavioral tendencies. As these potentialities vary, it seems conceivable that any reaction type might be found in any ethnic milieu. Also, it is evident that even the most primitive homogeneous group consists of individuals distinguished by their personal characteristics.

No matter how basic the discrepancies that directly concern the individual's impulses, ego functions and behavior are the main stream fed by these three tributaries: congenitally predetermined tendencies and reactions, social interaction, and the individual's response within the framework of a given environment.

Among the natives mentioned here, sadism and homosexual relationships belong to the normal cultural pattern. Whatever the motives for these acts, the sexual intercourse of a man and a young initiand must be considered a substitute gratification, in these cases triggered by counterphobic forces. Yet, despite the fact that these practices belong to the standard cultural organization, they have to be labeled perversions because the aggressive discharge and pleasure are *experienced genitally and through ejaculation.*

Once a perversion has become the custom or has been institutionalized, there is the danger that it might obscure the meaning of "normality." However, any concept of what is "normal" should be arrived at not by standards suggested by society—the legal codification of cultural expectations—but by genetic criteria as they have been developed in clinical and bio-psychological research.

The adjustment and self-control of an adult individual to a given environment or cultural standard is conditioned by his autonomous handling of instinctual aims. In addition to the fearlessness cited by Ernest Jones as a criterion for normality, such emotional requirements as object-cathexis and undisturbed identification, plus consistent genitality, are important. Essentially, these qualities, regardless of the culture, characterize the "normal" personality.

REFERENCES

1 Elias, Norbert. Über den Prozess der Zivilisation, Vol. I. Basel, 1939.

2 The Ladies Dictionary, Being a General Entertainment for the Fair-Sex. A Work Never Attempted Before in English. London, 1694.

3 Thomas, William I. Sex and Society. 4th impr., Chicago, 1913.

4 Wirz, Paul. Die Marind-anim von Hollaendisch-Sued-Neu-Guinea, Vol. II. Hamburg, 1925. Vol. I. Hamburg, 1922.

5 ———. loc. cit., Vol. I.

6 Williams, F. E. Papuans of the Trans-Fly. Oxford, 1936.

7 Róheim, Géza. "Unpublished Fieldnotes from Central Australia."

8 Deacon, A. Bernard. Malekula. London, 1934.

9 Westermark, Edward. *Ritual and Belief in Morocco*, Vol. I. London, 1926.

10 Grinnell, George B. *The Cheyenne Indians*. New Haven, 1923.

11 Parsons, Elsie C. "The Zuni La'mana." *American Anthropologist*, Vol. XVIII.

12 Benedict, Ruth F. *Patterns of Culture*. London, 1936.

13 Devereux, George. "Institutionalized Homosexuality of the Mohave Indians." *Human Biology*, Vol. IX.

14 Chabot, H. Th. *Verwantschap, Stand en Sexe in Zuid-Celebes*. Groningen-Djakarta, 1950.

15 Erikson, Erik H. *Childhood and Society*. New York, 1950.

16 Jones, Ernest. "The Concept of a Normal Mind." *Papers on Psycho-Analysis*. London, 1948.

17 Freud, Sigmund. "Analysis Terminable and Interminable." *Coll. Papers*, Vol. V. London, 1950.

18 Kubie, Lawrence S. "The Fundamental Nature of the Distinction Between Normality and Neurosis." *Psychoanalytic Quarterly*, Vol. XXIII, 1954.

II

Homosexuality

On Homosexuality

SANDOR S. FELDMAN

Reviewing, as thoroughly as one person can, the psychoanalytic literature on homosexuality since Freud's fundamental *Three Contributions to the Theory of Sex*, one can distinctly discern two points of view which, in one important aspect, are on common ground.

Both views find in homosexuality conflicts with the environment. However, because such conflicts are present in all other neurotic diseases, one cannot consider them as specific to homosexuality. Therefore it is assumed that bisexuality, the existence of which is taken for granted, is constitutionally stronger in those in whom life-conflicts result in homosexuality.

The other view, on the contrary, neglects when it does not reject the concept of bisexuality and other so-called constitutional factors; it lays emphasis on object-relationship which, as it turns out, can be assumed to be present from the beginning of life, regardless of whether an ego-state already exists or in what state the infantile ego might be. Those who hold this view are apparently satisfied with the depth and results of their investigations into the very early object-relationship conflicts, and do not need the concept of bisexuality. They reason that, even should bisexuality be a fact, it would not in itself explain

why only certain persons become homosexual; and that, furthermore, good therapeutic results prove that constitution, as far
as homosexuality is concerned, does not determine the final fate
of the individual. Psychoanalysts of the group who hold this
view leave open the problem of choice (option) of neurosis
or perversion, preferring to wait until further work gives the
answer to this question, too. I believe that, at this point, I
might offer some suggestions. In doing so, I am inclined to follow the second point of view. I realize that concepts such as
bisexuality, constitutional factors, autoeroticism, narcissism,
penis envy, etc., have to be reviewed. This necessity was expressed by Heinz Hartmann and Robert Knight, in 1948 and
1953 respectively.[1]

Many authors, including the writer, have found that: (1)
libido is already object-directed in the oral stage; this neces-
sitates a review of the concept and phenomenon of autoeroticism, the meaning of thumb-sucking, and narcissism; (2)
genitality, in both sexes, is already present in all the so-called
pregenital phases of sexual development; (3) signs of heterosexual object-relation-directedness, in both sexes, are present
from the very beginning of life. This would make bisexuality
a symptom of and not a predisposition to homosexuality.
Furthermore, it would reduce to a minimum the role of constitutional factors in homosexuality and the other perversions. In
addition, it would indicate that the penis envy of women is
not a cause but a result of conflicts which might lead to homosexuality or to other forms of perversion.[2]

The writer's proposition is as follows: *In the infant, the
genitalization of the pregenital erotogenic zones is already
present. In addition to their own libidinal cathexis, this gives
the erotogenic zones an orgastic potentiality.* This proposition
would, in my opinion, explain the individual's quest, in the
pregenital stages, for orgastic gratification. In the pregenital

stages, the more frustrated the child is, for whatever reasons, the more he needs the comfort of sensual gratification. If the child is loved and made happy, genitality will likewise come to the fore, just as well as in frustration; in this case, however, it is a straight and smooth process without the painful memory of frustration. By the addition of orgastic pleasure to the libidinous cathexis of the functions of self-preservation, the child achieves sensual gratification. This would explain the passive-anal libidinous position of the male child in a life-situation anxiety. The memory of this position is retained and again put to use in later years for the same reason. Let us not forget that the passive homosexual male in any form of homosexual practice strives for genital orgasm, as do female homosexuals. The truth of this has been demonstrated to the writer by the analysis of patients, some of whom will be presented in this paper. The genital orgastic addition to the libidinous cathexis of the functions of self-preservation in the pregenital phase blends together the instinct of self-preservation, sexuality and the individual's participation in the maintenance of the species. In a paper on *Ticklishness*, not yet published, I have demonstrated the interplay between the self-preservative and sexual instincts in reference to genital-orgastic gratification. My proposition might be considered an attempt to eliminate the existing confusion about the concepts of libido, eros, sexuality and life-instinct; it provides a basis for maintaining the fifty-year-old libido theory of Freud.*

Hermann discusses the importance of distinguishing between the different libido qualities.[3] Reich carries this further[4] when he states that kissing in love-making gratifies oral-libido; originally the goal was sucking but, in kissing, it is raised to the genital level. This transition from sucking to kissing is due

* The value of Freud's libido theory is historically, theoretically and practically so great that the writer adheres to it.

to the influence of genitality on oral eroticism. This helps us
to understand fellatio performed between two homosexuals
for genital-orgastic gratification.

The tendency to solve conflicts through genital orgasm has
already been emphasized by other authors: Hermann, Ferenczi,
Rado and Reich.[5] The writer—as do Fairbairn, Silverberg, A.
Balint, M. Balint and others—concentrates his attention on the
concept that the libido is, from the beginning, object-directed.
Though both sexes are cared for by a female, the mother, at
the oral stage of development, *there are already signs that both
the boy and the girl behave toward the mother as if she were
a heterosexual love-object.* Heterosexuality is an anatomically
inborn and inevitable fate of both sexes. The infant, cared for
by the mother, is forced to choose mother as a love-object. The
boy is given a heterosexual love-object from birth; the girl has
later to turn away from mother toward father. To the new-
born, father and mother can represent either sex. The boy
behaves toward a male who cares for him and feeds him with a
bottle as if he were a female. It naturally takes time until the
ego's reality-testing catches up with the facts. This again clearly
indicates that the male, due to his anatomy and biology, is
destined toward a female object and the female toward a male
object. This is of paramount importance for the understanding
of homosexuality in both sexes. Whether we deal with a male
or female homosexual, the oral-mother-object relationship is
found to be a conspicuous feature in the majority of cases. To
Bergler,[6] this is the core of the whole problem. I believe that
orality can become a "rescue station" of genitality, like the
other pregenital stages, and not only, as Bergler states, the
reverse.

I trust that my case presentations will demonstrate that
homosexuals, regardless of the great variation of the clinical

picture in overt and latent homosexuality in both sexes, have started as heterosexuals but that some traumatic situation—not a single traumatic event—forced them to achieve their originally heterosexual gratification through the detour of homosexuality.[7] All writers emphasize strongly that analyses of homosexuals disclose that there was a time when they had strong heterosexual feelings and sensations.

It is the consensus of many contemporary psychoanalytic workers that permanent homosexuals, like all perverts, are neurotics. Then the important problem of the choice of neurosis arises. Let us not forget that there is rarely a neurosis without some perversion and rarely a perversion without some neurotic symptoms. This paper concerns itself only with homosexuals with no endocrine disturbances who desire to be cured; we know little, analytically, about those who do not want to be cured even when they seek treatment for other neurotic symptoms. In such cases, the analysis has had to be given up.*

The problems are: When will a neurosis develop without a perversion and when a perversion-neurosis? If a perversion develops, what produces homosexuality rather than another kind of perversion?

The homosexual is the most mature of all perverts; he can love the object. All other perverts, overtly at least, have little or no *direct* contact with the object. Though all perverts, in the last analysis, *could* be and are in contact with an object, many of them seemingly intend in phantasy to destroy the object or be destroyed by it. In overt homosexuals, the love is manifest.

Returning to the problem of choice (option) of neurosis or perversion, I have found that, *whenever in childhood or adult-*

---

* In one case of male homosexuality, the analysis (in agreement with the patient) was given up because an alarming paranoid delusion of persecution emerged from its latent state in the transference situation.

hood the individual's life-love-position became insecure, a perversion developed; whenever guilt became the prevalent feature, a neurosis developed; when both threats were present, neurosis and perversion developed. Pregenital manifestations characterize the perversions, but less so in homosexuals than in other perverts. *Whenever, in the pregenital phase of sexual development, a pregenital contact with a heterosexual object was permitted, perversion-neurosis developed; if not, homosexual neurosis developed.*

In both the perversions and the neuroses, anxiety is the central feature. To have a secure love-position is more important than not to be guilty. Primarily, the individual wants to secure his love-position, and only secondarily does he bother about guilt feelings. It is in the pregenital period of life when, in a physical sense, love-position with bodily contact is established. Guilt, on the other hand, is rather a phenomenon of the genital and post-genital stages. The homosexual, though through a detour, has maintained a strong object-contact.

Presentation of brief case histories will give the writer an opportunity to elaborate in somewhat more detail the views expressed above. Naturally, only those features of the case analyses pertinent to the subject will be presented. Let us begin with homosexuality in females.

Case Presentations of Homosexuality in Females

[1]

This is pertinent material from the case history of a young woman, a virgin. When she was about four, her mother, thinking they were necessary, insisted on giving her enemas. Although she disliked the enemas, she was nevertheless pleased that her mother gave them to her; she interpreted it as evidence that her mother was interested in her and loved her. At about the age of nine, she became aware of the fact that the mother gave her enemas not because she loved her but because she found pleasure in giving them. (This somewhat strange statement was confirmed when the writer later learned more of the family.) After that, no force could make her accept the enemas from her mother. But she took them secretly herself, imagining that another woman, not the mother who disappointed her but one who loved her, was giving it. As time went on, this practice became accompanied by genital masturbation.

Once, as a child, she visited a playmate who was sitting on her mother's lap with her head on the mother's bosom. Filled with envy, she later asked her mother to hold her thus, but was refused and ridiculed. From then on, again secretly, she played the scene with her dolls, holding them to her bosom.

The mother paid special attention to an older boy in the family. This boy often teased the patient by pointing to his erect penis in his pants. She envied the boy because mother loved him more; she envied the boy's penis because he was so proud of it.

On entering analysis, she showed an incredibly intense penis-envy; she wanted to take it away, to tear it off, to keep it, to squeeze it. But she did not want to be a boy, a male. She liked being a woman and there was nothing masculine in her appearance or behavior. What she wanted was to possess something she could be proud of: a penis, beautiful breasts, money, etc. She was suspicious of men and thought that they wanted only her body without "really" loving her. To prove that he loved her, a man must be willing to give her presents and spend money on her without wanting her body. She was fascinated when she saw beautiful girls with beautiful "proud" breasts; a favorite and permanent sensual fantasy was of two beautiful girls playing with their beautiful breasts.

This girl did not feel loved by her mother from the very beginning. Therefore her main aim was to establish by whatever means a happy life-situation for herself. To this end, because of the experiences described above, she chose the following: to have the breasts of her mother or, later on, their substitutes; to have in her possession the penis of which men are so proud; to receive enemas from women who loved her.*

This picture enables us to examine the phenomena of breast-attachment, autoeroticism, penis-envy and anal-eroticism in a woman. I have observed, from this and other cases, that the breast is the primary representative of the love-object in both sexes. If one's life-position is safe, i.e., if one is loved and important enough to be loved, then from this secure love-position there is an unobstructed way to the acceptance of the biologically suitable heterosexual love-object. If the love-object-position is not safe, then it has to be established in phantasy and in "perverted" object relations. This case illustrates the view-point of some psychoanalytic workers, including the writer, that autoeroticism is blended at a very early stage with object-love relationship. If the latter is not secure, normal orgastic gratification cannot take place. Whatever provides this safety, earlier or later, opens the way for the genital orgastic process. From such observations, perhaps one is entitled to draw the conclusion that narcissism is the libido-cathexis of the ego flowing into the ego from early libidinous object gratification, i.e., from the security the infant derives, in the sense of being important enough to be loved (and not in the sense of Adler). Long ago, I. Hermann expressed the view that narcissism cannot be a primary phenomenon. According to him, though clinging to the mother cannot yet be considered as love, nevertheless it is the ground from which love will sprout. This love can turn

* This patient never developed overt homosexuality; nevertheless, her case is discussed in this paper to show the steps which, in other cases, might lead to overt homosexuality.

into narcissism through external influences—traumatic disappointments.[8]

The same concept applies to thumb-sucking, which returns later as fellatio in both sexes. The thumb represents the first love-object, the mother, and can later be represented by any person, male or female. From this period on, the infant is searching for the love-object, to find it again via the genitals.

Penis-envy seems to be a secondary envy. If there is primary envy, the child will lose it easily, provided the primary object-love situation is satisfactory.

This young woman did not practice homosexuality. She did not develop into an overt Lesbian because the desire to be a "proud" woman was stronger in her than to be a man, "proud" of his penis.

[II]

This is a woman who, in late adolescence, was stimulated by an overt homosexual woman older than herself with whom for several years she had an intense sexual relationship. The patient also had a sexual relationship with a man whom she loved very much and who loved her equally. She could never achieve orgasm in the heterosexual relationship unless she was locally stimulated by the man. She could not "let herself go" with him because she felt that she was loved "only" because she was a woman for the man; with the woman, for practical reasons, only manual stimulation was possible to achieve orgasm.

In contrast to her reaction when with the man, she was very passionate with the woman. The other woman was the active partner. She adored the patient, loved her passionately, admired all the things she did and stood for. The patient did not need to do anything to be loved. She was loved by the other woman "just for herself"; there were no duties and no conditions were attached; she had only to exist and to permit the woman to love her. It would have been complete bliss if she had not been tormented by the feeling that it was an abnormal thing which had to remain forever a secret. She would not be able to divulge it to a husband, to her children, nor to anyone in the world but the analyst.

She had been an utterly neglected and unattractive child. She had been excluded from the company of girls, and later, no man cared to be with her. Once she was ardently in love with a young man but he did not even take cognizance of her. She received no support whatever from her parents or siblings. She felt inferior, ugly, lonely, desperately abandoned and unhappy. This was her state of mind when she met the passionate, overtly homosexual woman for whom she was everything in the world—wonderful, beautiful, sparkingly witty, etc. Swept off her feet, she yielded to the woman's sensual advances and entered into an ardent sexual love-relationship with her.

In her sexual relationship with the man, she could not be orgastically satisfied because he was a man and therefore it was natural and not extraordinary that he should desire her, love her, and even admire her. Her relationship with him could not compensate for all her frustrations in childhood and adulthood. Consequently, she could not achieve sensual gratification during intercourse with him except through manual genital stimulation. But there was no bliss in this gratification. The woman's love was unusual, extraordinary; she convinced the patient of something she had never felt before, that she was someone important. In the homosexual relation, for reasons of anatomy, only manual genital stimulation could take place but here it was blissful.

This seemed to me an instructive case. From the time she was very young, the patient waited for a man who would make her feel important. Such a man did not appear. In any event, it might have been too late, as indeed it turned out to be later; a relationship with a man could no longer erase the accumulated feelings of resentment and frustration. She met a homosexual woman who restored her faith in herself by making her feel important, i.e., worthy of being loved, and she became homosexual, at the same time maintaining her relationship with the man. The homosexual relationship lasted for years, but because of her guilt and fear of discovery, she abruptly ended it. The break was followed by several phobic symptoms.

Her guilt about the homosexual relationship was not present at the beginning. Because the woman made her happy, guilt was brushed aside and did not cause any symptoms. But she was too healthy to tolerate the relationship indefinitely. The moment she ended it, fears emerged and again she felt inferior, lonely and unattractive, and, in addition, she felt she was abnormal.

There were no traces of masculinity in this woman. In the homosexual relationship, she did not need to behave as a man; she was enjoyed by her partner as a complete woman.[9] There were no signs of bisexuality. She would have been completely satisfied with a man had she felt that she had a place in life. Without the feeling of a safe self, her ego could not permit a biologically adequate sexual relationship but only a relationship which restored her self-esteem.

[III]

Concurrently with orgastically passionate relationships with men, a married woman had a sexual relationship with a woman older than herself. The latter had large breasts which greatly interested the patient. The two loved one another. Their love-play ended with mutual masturbation. The patient had always been interested in breasts and had had several homosexual ex-

periences with girls while in college. The breasts were always
in the center of the love-play. Usually, the homosexual episode
was initiated by the other girl in rehearsing passionate necking
with a boy.

The patient's trouble started with the birth of a brother. She
could not "stand" seeing her brother at her mother's breast;
she felt neglected. When she became aware of the anatomical
difference between the sexes, she thought that the boy was
preferred by the mother. She cried bitterly and, as compensation,
she invented a special masturbatory play in which she imagined
she had an extremely long penis. A certain object was inserted
into the vagina and pulled out again repeatedly. This resulted in
vaginal orgasm.

Was this woman bisexual? No. Was her penis-envy an innate
resentment over the fact that she was a girl rather than a boy?
No. She was from head to toe a perfect woman and she liked
being a woman. What was missing then? Why did she want
a penis? Why did she enjoy a relationship with a motherly
woman? Because she thought that a boy was more appreciated
and loved than a girl. She wanted a secure love-life-position.
Of this, in phantasy, the penis-envy and the homosexual relationship assured her and she obtained an additional vaginal orgasm
via a detour. The homosexual relationship was given up with
no special effort.

[IV]

This female patient at first denied any memory of heterosexual feeling but, in the course of analysis, she admitted that
as a young girl she was interested sexually in men.

She was a "perfect" Lesbian. She did not seek treatment
because of the sexual aberration, as she was happy in being
homosexual and men meant nothing to her from a sexual point

of view. She wanted help because of her jealousy, which "drove her crazy" whenever one of her girl friends became interested in another woman. She took the masculine role in the relationship. Usually, her female partner wanted it also and, eventually, a compromise took place in which each would enjoy it in turn. The patient was fascinated by the genitals of her female partner and could have gazed at them for hours. When sufficiently aroused, they would imitate intercourse between a man and a woman or orgasm would be achieved through cunnilingus.

When she realized that her unbearable jealousy could not be cured without analyzing the causes of her homosexuality, this patient withdrew from treatment and committed herself to an institution. She got in touch with the analyst several times, reporting her condition. Shock treatment, as far as the writer knows, did not help. She became panicky at the overt signs of strong heterosexual feelings in the transference situation.

This patient was an only child. There were violent scenes between the parents, which were very distressing to her. She did not feel secure with her parents. Love for her father was always present. When she was scarcely out of childhood, her mother constantly complained to her about the father: that he was drinking, that he ran after girls, that he was wild about women, etc. She spied upon her father and found that her mother's charges were true. This was a great shock to her. The mother warned her against men, saying that they wanted only sensuality, abandoned their wives soon after marriage, and so forth. Analysis disclosed that the female partner represented not the mother but the girls whom the father would run after. The patient identified herself with the father and made love to the girls as he did. She was "wild about women" like her father. The only difference was that she was "faithful" to her partner, and looked for another only if she were dropped. This was preceded by a state of jealousy. Her homosexuality meant: "I do not need a man (father) who abandoned me (like father); I myself am a man (father)." She lived in a "true marriage" with the beloved girl, took the man's role and wore a "wedding ring."[10]

[v]

This woman who, in adolescence, had engaged in mutual genital play with several girls became sexually excited as a grownup if she looked at pictures of beautiful female bodies. With men, she was completely frigid. Intercourse with men disgusted her; though she might become interested in a new man, she was frigid in intercourse with him. In her unhappy childhood, she interpreted her austere father's utterly disinterested attitude toward her, as a female, to her ugliness (she was in fact not ugly but the opposite) and to the fact that her mother was beautiful. She felt unable to cope with her mother not only in respect to her father but in relation to all men. She felt that any woman was more beautiful than herself and gave up any hope of being able to attract a man as other women did. If she did attract a man, she could not believe it and remained frigid. She turned, in phantasy, to women. She identified herself with attractive women who could "really" attract men. Behind all those beautiful women was herself, secure and safe; it was a heterosexual gratification via homosexuality.

Case Presentations of Homosexuality in Males

[I]

This male grammar-school teacher, close to thirty, had no interest in women and no previous relationship with them.

He was interested only in small boys. Gradually, he had become panicky about this sensual interest and afraid that, unable to resist, he might seduce a boy, something he had never done. He felt that he should not stay in his profession unless he were cured. To interest him, the boys had to be seven to eight years old. Younger or older boys did not attract him at all.* It was important to him that these young boys should be interested in women, phantasy about them, and have erections while doing so. When this happened, he felt a strong sensual urge to touch the boy's penis. This was his masturbatory phantasy. He was not interested in any other kind of homosexual practice. The key to understanding this fortunate case was offered in the very early stage of the short analysis through a dream. In this dream he was "observing a boy, about the age of eight," in bed. In the adjacent room, the parents' bedroom, were the parents in bed. The connecting door was open. The boy in bed was observing, through revealing sounds, the sexual intercourse of the parents (the "primal scene") and, due to this, became sexually aroused and had an erection. The dreamer felt a strong desire to touch the boy's penis. He did so and awakened with a seminal discharge.

When it was suggested that he himself might have observed his parents' sexual intercourse, a memory emerged; it was at the same age, the age of eight, and in exactly the same setting as in the dream that he witnessed the sexual intercourse of his parents, became aroused, had an erection and masturbated. He wanted to do as his father had done, sleep with a woman, the mother. The homosexual detour expressed a strong heterosexual (incestuous) desire.

* The writer has found that cases in which such specific conditions are present are prognostically good.

[II]

This overtly homosexual man appreciated women aestheti-
cally but had no sexual interest in them. Whenever a woman
got close to seducing him, he became panicky and withdrew.
The idea of making love to a woman horrified him and he had
a dread of the female genitals. (However, there were definite
recollections of interest in women in early childhood.) Only
strong and young heterosexual males interested him sensually.
He was utterly indifferent to homosexual males. In becoming
acquainted with a young man, he first investigated whether
the boy was interested in having intercourse with a girl. When
he had made sure of this, and the knowledge aroused him to
the point of erection and orgastic desire, he would take the
boy to a prostitute and encourage him to make love to her.
As the boy had intercourse with her, the patient would rub
himself on the boy's buttocks until he himself achieved orgastic
seminal discharge. Often it was not even necessary to take the
boy to a woman; it was enough to talk about the boy's desire
to have intercourse with a woman. He would then touch
the erect penis of the boy and call on him to participate in
mutual masturbation or fellatio.

Why this man needed another man between him and the
woman was disclosed in the course of the analysis. The boy
represented himself, and the condition for being free to engage
in heterosexual gratification was the encouragement of another
man, represented by himself. He had *not* received such encouragement. On the contrary, in his early childhood and
young adulthood, he was under the influence of a man several
years his senior, a strongly heterosexual, influential member of
the family who liked the patient and who warned him that a
nice boy did not desire such ugly sexual things. The patient

chose young men of the same age difference as had existed between himself and the strong man in his family, and he did the opposite: he encouraged the man to do that "ugly thing," i.e., to make love to a woman.

This was an unsuccessful case; the analysis, as was mentioned earlier in this paper, had to be interrupted because an alarming paranoid persecutory panic emerged in the positive transference-situation.

The patient never produced a delusion of persecution with a man with whom he had an overt homosexual relationship or when his love, without physical relationship, was tacitly accepted by the other man. Only when there was no response from the other did the paranoid delusional state develop. It was so not only in the transference situation but with several other men, indicating that the homosexual feeling need not be repressed or latent in order for a delusional paranoid feeling to emerge. The frustration of the homosexual desire is sufficient. At least, it was so in this instructive case.

[III]

Already in early childhood, this patient was a very unhappy boy. He carried within him the feeling that nothing he did could be good. It was to no avail that, in the course of time, he became successful—in school, in his profession, etc.; the feeling that he was "just not good" stayed with him and depressed him so much that he often thought seriously of suicide.

Though he had had no overt homosexual experiences, he considered himself to have passive homosexual desires. In fact, he became panicky when a friend playfully "goosed" him. He had a feeling that he was biologically queer, a misfit, a mixture of male and female, that he was neither male nor female because he was both. And, therefore, he was no good and had no justification for existing; he had no place in the world; the best thing for him was to perish.

The feeling of being both male and female was attributed by him to his physical appearance. He saw himself as conspicuously feminine (which was not the case at all) and as having large buttocks, he stressed particularly the fact that, during sexual intercourse, his orgasm was much more satisfactory when, at his request, his female partner would place her finger in his anus.

He was an only child and his parents often expressed their desire to have a girl as well. They were happy that they had him, a boy, but were unhappy in not having a girl, too. At any rate, the patient thought that they were unhappy in looking at him because then they realized what they had missed in not having a girl. In his feelings, this situation made his position, in the family and in life, uncertain. He attempted, in childhood, to solve his parents' problem—and his own—by behaving at times like a girl; so much so, that his father often corrected him for it. It did not work in childhood and, naturally, even less when he grew up.

In this case, I concluded that the patient's feeling of being bisexual was psychologically determined; that, in addition to its own erogenicity, the anus was raised to the genital level because, in his uncertain life-position, the need arose to possess a feminine-like sex organ, the anus; that the tendency toward passive homosexuality originated from the need to solve a life-problem.

[IV]

The following material is part of the history of the analysis of a young male patient who was completely incapacitated and who once committed himself to an institution for ten months in an attempt to find rest. He was "confused" and "bewildered." The analysis was successful.

A grave infantile neurosis had been present from the age of one and a half. It persisted and was overlapped, after late puberty, by a neurotic condition which manifested itself in lack of sexual excitement with women, complete impotency, and in "feminine feelings" toward men.

The patient's statement that his sickness started with an anxiety dream was confirmed by the parents. The dream was recovered during the analysis and it represented the primal scene. Following the dream, he had awakened in great anxiety, trembling and crying, and his mother had taken him in her arms and comforted him. He interpreted the sexual intercourse of his parents as a cruel fight between them. The cruelty excited him and stirred up an aggressive feeling within him. Persistent depression followed; the analysis of his reaction to aggressive impulses was an essential part of his analysis. He could not be aggressive in any situation. Yet no matter how he adhered to this peaceful attitude, he felt that he was potentially a murderer. He liked women but could not be aroused by them. He visited prostitutes, was nice to them, put his head on their bosoms, cried bitterly, and left. He did what he had done on awakening from his dream in infancy; he cried on his mother's bosom. Sexual intercourse between a man and a woman was considered by him as a murderous action on the part of both partners. In early puberty (having only one sibling, a brother, and disregarding the fact that, in some families, there are more than two children), he thought that a man can have intercourse with a woman only twice in his lifetime and that each intercourse cost him a testicle. When he observed little girls squatting, the clitoris appeared to him as a protruding weapon which, during intercourse, would enter the urethra, proceed into the scrotum and pull out one testicle which would be drawn into the woman and create pregnancy.

The patient's brother was an overt homosexual. As such, he had been discovered and had lost his professional and social position. On at least one occasion, he had seduced the patient and had played with his penis. The patient enjoyed it. The memory remained as a constant desire and, sexually, it was this he was yearning for. This was his great depressing secret. He was waiting in desire and fear for his brother to come and play with him again. Later, other men were substituted for the brother.

He was ambivalent toward his parents. They were kind and loving; so he loved them. They were cruel, having sexual intercourse; father was a hunter and mother killed chickens and offered the meat for consumption. He himself was cruel because he would have liked to have sexual intercourse with women, because he ate meat, because he would go to war and kill.

What he always wanted was to be with his mother as a baby with his head on her breast. But his father was in the way. Father loved mother and was always with her. In a dream, the patient saw a dog faithfully following mother; he was jealous and called the dog away from mother; the dog followed him but his aim was to be with mother and not with the dog; he tried to get rid of the dog but the dog "stuck" to him. Naturally, the faithful dog was father. The patient was overnice and respectful toward him. As it finally came out, he wanted to turn father (men) away from mother (women); the original love-object was and remained the mother.

Almost all the pregenital and pre-Oedipal, genital and Oedipal manifestations (known from our analyses and from analytic literature) were present: autoeroticism, oral-anal-genital sadism, urethral eroticism, castration fear, etc. Nevertheless, one could clearly see that, from very early infancy, the original sexual object was the female. She could not be reached smoothly and directly. The patient needed to make various detours to follow his healthy sexual tendency. Even the patient knew this all the time—as he realized toward the end of the analysis.

[v]

This was a classical analytical case. The patient was an "analytical textbook." From the complicated history of a grave neurosis, I shall emphasize only the essential material pertinent to our present subject.

The patient was a grown man when he first permitted another man to perform fellatio with him. He was potent with women. However, he could never achieve such a high degree of orgastic gratification with women as he did in his masturbatory phantasies in which he imagined he was a woman, his skin, his "breasts" being fondled. In addition, he often inserted various objects into his anus.

The attitude of his orally frustrating mother, a socially very respected father, and events which he interpreted as frightening castration-threats did not permit him to abandon autoeroticism and narcissism. Both manifestations were extremely prominent in his whole life. Let us not forget that, in his autoeroticism, he figured as a woman, a heterosexual object whom he could not possess because castration-fear forced him to identify with her and reach her through such a disguise. In my opinion, one cannot well understand such cases nor, perhaps, the neuroses and psychoses without using the concept of "as-if." This patient behaved "as-if" he were a woman—his activity included transvestism—but this was only a "faulty adjustment," an "arrangement," a "technique" necessitated by an insecure life-position that did not permit a healthy object-relationship. Even his narcissism casts doubt on whether it is right to assume the existence of a "primary narcissism." As I saw in this and other cases, the narcissism means that the patient loves himself as he would like to love the object which is forbidden to him. This has been proven by the fact that the so-called narcissistic neuroses have become accessible to therapy like the transference neuroses.

Therapy of Homosexuals

No matter how "objective" the therapist is, his conception of humanity will play a mighty role in the way he leads the patient toward a solution of his problems. It is *his* objective therapy, right or wrong. No one has said or can say the last word in science. I have presented what I believe today. In the course of many years, failures and successes in the treatment of homosexuals have convinced me that, at least for me, the comparatively best technique is as follows:

1. I start with the justified premise—justified through clinical experience—that, unless demonstrable pathology is present, human beings are born, *by and large*, with such equipment as to fulfill their biological, social and ethical tasks in life.

2. Because homosexuals have, or would like to have, a close *personal* contact with the love-object of the same sex and because, usually, their aim is an orgastic-genital gratification, it is comparatively not difficult to show them that something alien has inserted itself between them and a heterosexual object, that they were compelled to place a defense-structure over the biologically determined natural foundation. When a man chooses a love-partner with feminine traits or is aroused by a

man in women's clothing or by a girl in man's clothing, does he not want the female in the disguise of a man? When a man, disappointed in the female genitals, loves not women but men as girls do, is there not present, behind this identification, his original love for women? When a man identifies himself with a boy of the age he himself was when he desired to be loved by his mother as he now loves this boy, is this not heterosexual love under a thinly veiled disguise?

As a practitioner, I have learned that, essentially, homosexuals want to mate with the opposite sex. In therapy, my intention is to discover what kind of fear or distress diverted the patient from the straight line and made a devious detour necessary. Whatever the patient offers is taken into consideration, but regression, fixation, "attachment," identification, pregenital erotogenic zones, narcissism, autoeroticism, etc., are stations only secondary in importance to the main part of the therapy, which is to emphasize that the patient's original position is a healthy one, given as a precious gift by nature.

Most of the patients have a favored condition which, if fulfilled, provides them with orgasm. In this condition is contained the explanation of why the homosexual had to choose a perverted way to his sexual gratification. The perversion is analyzed not for the sake of understanding the perversion itself but to find the *meaning* of the perversion, to find the life-situation which forced the individual to choose homosexuality as the only way to sexual relationship with another human being. The earlier the individual found himself in a distressful life-situation, the farther will his orgastic position be from the biologically normal relationship. The analyst has to deal with such material but bears in mind always that his real goal is to bring the patient to the biologically given heterosexual relationship which is not *created* by the therapy but *liberated* for use. This attitude on the part of the analyst is the most powerful weapon against the resistances of the patient. The homosexual will, for a while at least, stubbornly insist that he is a "born homosexual," that he must have been born a queer person, a misfit, a mixture of male and female, that homosexuality remains for him the only route to sexual gratification. That is all untrue. The more convinced the analyst is that an underlying natural personal relationship in sexual and in other ways is present, the more likely will the patient come to the same conclusion as the analyst: that man is born for woman and woman is born for man. Anything else in the picture means only that, once upon a time, a trouble arose which diverted the individual from his normal path in life.

REFERENCES

1   Hartmann, Heinz. "Comments on the Psychoanalytic Theory Of The Instinctual Drives." *Psychoanalytic Quarterly*, Vol. XVII, No. 3, 1948.

    Knight, Robert. *Bulletin of the Menninger Clinic*, Vol. XVII, No. 1, 1953.

2   Klein, Melanie. "The Oedipus Complex in the Light of Early Anxieties." *International Journal of Psychoanalysis*, Vol. XXVI, 1945.

    Fenichel, Otto. *The Psychoanalytic Theory of Neurosis*. New York, 1945.

    Rado, Sandor. "An Adaptational View of Sexual Behavior." *Psychosexual Development in Health and Disease*. New York, 1949.

    Horney, Karen. "The Denial of the Vagina." *International Journal of Psychoanalysis*, Vol. XIV, 1933.

    Fairbairn, W. Ronald. *Psychoanalytic Studies of the Personality*. With a Preface by Ernest Jones. London, 1952.

Greenacre, Phyllis. "Pregenital Patterning." *International Journal of Psychoanalysis*, Vol. XXXIII, Part 4, 1952.

Freud, Sigmund. *Three Contributions to the Theory of Sex*. New York, 1910.

Reich, Wilhelm. *Die Funktion des Orgasmus*. Leipzig, 1927.

Sterba, Richard. *Introduction to the Psychoanalytic Theory of the Libido*. New York, 1942.

Winnicott, D. W. "Transitional Objects and Transitional Phenomena." *International Journal of Psychoanalysis*, Vol. XXXIV, Part 2, 1953.

Sadger, J. "Allerlei Gedanken zur Psychopathia Sexualis." *Neue Aerztliche Zentralzeitung*, 1919.

Stekel, W. *Onanie und Homosexualitaet*. Berlin-Wien, 1923.

Balint, Michael. "Early Developmental States of the Ego—Primary Object Love." *International Journal of Psychoanalysis*, Vol. XXX, Part 4, 1949.

Friedjung, J. K. *Onanie*. Wisebaden, 1912.

Petoe, Endre. "Infant and Mother: Observations on Object-Relations in Early Infancy." *International Journal of Psychoanalysis*, Vol. XXX, Part 4, 1949.

Balint, Alice. "Love for the Mother and Mother-Love." *International Journal of Psychoanalysis*, Vol. XXX, Part 4, 1949.

Schaxel, Hedwig. "In sonderheft-Onanie." *Zeitschrift für Psychoanalytische Paedagogik*, Vol. II, 1928.

Silverberg, William V. *Childhood Experience and Personal Destiny*. New York, 1952.

Rado, Sandor. "A Critical Examination of the Concept of Bisexuality." *Psychosomatic Medicine*, Vol. II, 1940.

3   Hermann, Imre. "Zur Frage der Libidocriterien." *Imago*, Vol. XXIII, 1937.

4   Reich, Wilhelm. *Die Function des Orgasm*. Leipzig, 1927.

5   Hermann, Imre. *A Tudattalan Es Az Oesztoeoeknek Oervenyelmelete* (The Whirl Theory of the Unconscious and the Instincts). Budapest, 1934.

Ferenczi, Sandor "Thalassa: A Theory of Genitality." *Psychoanalytic Quarterly*, Vol. II, 1933.

6   Bergler, Edmund. *The Superego*. New York, 1912.

7   Hermann, Imre. *The Primordial Instincts of Man*. Budapest, 1943.

8   Deutsch, Helene. "On Female Homosexuality." *The Psychoanalytic Reader*, Vol. I. New York, 1948.

9   Bychowski, Gustav. "The Ego of Homosexuals." *International Journal of Psychoanalysis*, Vol. XXVI, Parts 3 and 4, 1945.

Nunberg, Hermann. "Homosexuality, Magic and Aggression." *Practice and Theory of Psychoanalysis*. New York, 1936.

Freud, Anna. "Some Clinical Remarks Concerning the Treatment of Cases of Male Homosexuality." *Bulletin of the American Psychoanalytic Association*, Vol. VII, No. 2, 1951.

Eidelberg, Ludwig. *An Outline of a Comparative Pathology of the Neuroses*. New York, 1954.

————. "Neurosis, A Negative of Perversion?" *Psychiatric Quarterly*, Vol. XXVIII, 1954.

Ovesey, Lionel. "The Homosexual Conflict." *Psychiatry*, Vol. XVII, No. 3, 1954.

Homosexuality and Psychosis

GUSTAV BYCHOWSKI

Observations on various forms of mental disturbance accompanied by homosexuality, or vice versa, on homosexuals manifesting symptoms of psychosis, have been known to classical, that is, pre-analytic psychiatry.[1] Yet it was not until the tool of psychoanalysis could be applied to our investigations that the connection between psychosis and homosexuality could become the subject of more than a purely descriptive study.

It seems that the first clinical description—suggesting a possible connection between psychosis and sexual inversion—appears in *De Prestigiis Daemonun*, the magnum opus by Weyer, the hero of what has been called the first psychiatric revolution (1563). "I knew another Sodomite who complained that he always heard passers-by come to cause noise in his ears; even his parents, he said, were doing it; he wrote to me on his own behalf, quite secretly asking me whether I could not give him some advice, since some people had told him that his trouble was in the organ of hearing."[2]

With the advent of psychoanalysis and its impact on clinical psychiatry, the concept of psychotic symptoms developing as a defense of the ego against the awareness of homosexuality came into being. However, in Bleuler's monograph, we find this problem mentioned only briefly on two occasions.

A brief review of psychoanalytic contributions to the problems of psychosis and homosexuality should start with the classic contributions by Freud. He followed his pioneering study of Schreber's case (1911) by a comparative study of jealousy, paranoia and homosexuality (1912) and the study of a case of paranoia running counter to the psychoanalytic theory of the disease (1915). In the latter, he showed that even when the persecutor of a woman patient happened to be a man, he nevertheless was only a substitute for the maternal image.[3]

According to them, MacAlpine and Hunter, two British psychoanalysts, think that the change into a woman, which was one of the turning points in the development of Schreber's psychosis, "was not punishment by castration for forbidden homosexual wishes nor was it a means of achieving such wishes; rather its purpose was to permit procreation as a woman.

"Schreber's basic bisexuality had developed into a true manifest ambisexuality, male and female potentials being equally matched. Thus he developed fantasies of self-impregnation while he was acting the part of the woman having intercourse with himself."[6]

This penetrating reanalysis of Schreber's material reminds us of elements described in some former detailed clinical observations of schizophrenia, in particular the classic publications of Nunberg.[7]

The role of ambisexuality, with its far-reaching consequences in the clinical picture of advanced schizophrenia, has been evident for a long time. From a clinical point of view, one should bear in mind that Schreber not only went through periods of deep paranoid aggression and extensive elaboration but also long periods of catatonia. We know especially, from detailed observations of catatonic attacks and catatonic stupor, that phantasies of self-procreation frequently play an important part.

It is also generally recognized that confusion about one's own sexual identity is a frequent and important part of schizophrenic symptomatology. It may occur at a relatively early stage of the illness and, at times, may be detected by psychological testing prior to becoming manifest clinically. In my opinion, this symptom reflects a significant change in the patient's ego and may be described as a struggle of the feminine and masculine identification or, in other words, generally speaking, of the paternal versus the maternal introject.

Detailed observations of this process can best be gathered during analytic therapy of patients in a stage of incipient or even latent schizophrenia. They are supplemented by whatever data we can gather from the observation of frank psychotics. An additional source of information is provided by the analytic observation of patients subjected to insulin shock therapy.

I propose to illustrate the above-mentioned points by brief clinical notes.

The changes in the ego, in the initial stage of schizophrenia, often bear the characteristics of weakness, passivity and lessening of initiative. This basic impairment may, at an early stage, be interpreted by the patient in a delusional way as a result of hostile action by a person or persons in the outside world. In many cases, especially in young individuals, this initial feeling of persecution has a distinctly sexual character either as an attempt at rape or some form of castration. As to the original persecutor, that is, the initiator and the primary cause of the changes in the mental and the bodily ego, in these initial stages he appears very often as one of the parents of either sex.

The masochistic feminine core of this constellation is often perceived by the patient without any therapeutic interpretation. One of my patients of this group, while discussing his paranoid feelings which were originating, as it were, under my eyes, emphasized "his own role in giving people the opportunity to be on the top" by guessing their wishes and being penetrated by their most secret desires for loving but also dominating, overwhelming, humiliating and weakening him. In the future course of his development, the patient felt increasingly feminine both in his bodily sensations and in his general ego feeling. In school, he began to feel that he was being treated by his fellow students and instructors more as a girl than as a man and, at times, heard them referring to him as "a she."

Passive homosexual feelings began to dominate the transference situation and were warded off by fleeting ideas of reference and persecution. I shall return to this observation at a later point in the discussion of the structure of latent psychosis. For future reference, I shall call this patient Michael.

Such changes in the body ego, when further advanced, may result in the sensation of transformation into a female. Incidentally, we observe with much less frequency the delusion of transformation into a male in a woman. It would be incorrect to assume that such changes occur only in advanced clinical stages of frank schizophrenia. We observe them in initial stages in ambulatory or even latent schizophrenics, where we have the opportunity to study their structure and various shadings.

Generally speaking, we may say that these patients begin to feel, as it were, an invasion by a feminine body image, substituting in parts for their masculine self. Since the process, in my opinion, consists in the maternal introject trying to replace the paternal image, it is natural that, in most cases, the change starts with the breasts. They seem to grow and to assume the feminine shape. One may say that the patient's body ego tends to revert to its original identification with the maternal breast. One of these patients who, through his analysis, was being helped to recognize and free himself from this primitive incorporation, expressed it in the following words: "Had I really received my mother's love, then I would be like my mother and would have breasts." In his fear of being abandoned by his parents and thus left to the desolation of utter loneliness, he developed a set of phantasies in which he identified himself with both his father and his mother. In this way, phantasying himself as a hermaphrodite, he could maintain a state of pseudo-independence from both dangerous parental images. With the maternal outweighing by far the paternal identification, the patient had phantasies of being a woman and thus being threatened with sexual aggression by his father and paternal substitutes, including the analyst.

In 1930, I published an observation of a patient whose identification with the maternal breast went so far that he phantasied himself persecuted by both men and women who sucked him out as the infant sucks out the mother's breast. This case of oral paranoid delusion demonstrated the power and rigidity of this earliest identification.[8]

In many of these patients, homosexual submission is first sought and then dreaded as a means of establishing unity with the father. The feminine image imposes itself as a main component of the body image—or image of the self—and makes the patient feel as though he were a woman. The patient gives a detailed description of his feminine feelings; he imagines how his mother must be feeling toward his father and feels in the same way, his mother's way, toward other men and their genitals. As a result of this constellation, his ego becomes bombarded by passive homosexual cravings which he experiences either directly or in the form of fear, rage or paranoid projection. In the course of analytic working through, the feminine image of the self becomes externalized and fastened on other men, including the analyst. In his way he, can turn the tables for a short while and feel like a man while other men are turned into women.

A patient of this group experienced most vividly the incorporation of the mother of his early childhood. He felt an alien body in his stomach which contracted and quivered like a vagina. In his adolescence, he used to phantasy himself as a woman with a vaginal opening and a large phallus stuck into it. Pregnancy phantasies followed and were reacted to by horror. In identification with his mother, he took over a number of her abdominal sensations and, by a sort of visceral empathy, relived the physical suffering of his mother. The incorporation of the malevolent pre-Oedipal mother as a "bad object" resulted in a gamut of hypochondriacal symptoms and the idea of being poisoned, at first by his mother, then by his wife. The aggressive, domineering attitude of the mother, in particular the frequent enemas which she used to force upon him, contributed to creating a feminine image of himself being raped, as it were, by his mother. Considerable amounts of oral aggression had become invested in the maternal introject. In the course of analytic working through, they were released in the form of rage, directed at his mother, his wife and the analyst. Through projection, these individuals became invested with all this aggression so that the patient felt himself the object of their hostility and persecution. However, elements of passivity—spread over the entire body ego but especially concentrated in the anal region—made the patient into an object of homosexual persecution. As a manifestation of the ego-alien passive cravings, he developed painful anal itching. He used to hold back his excrements and avoided bodily ablutions in order not to deprive himself of the protection he fancied "dirt" gave him against anticipated homosexual attacks by his father, older brother and, through derivation, other men. At the same time, he was obviously satisfying the passive homosexual urge in an autoerotic way; here, too, he was trying to be self-sufficient in his own characteristically schizoid way.

In the course of the analytic process, the release of the male introject compelled the ego to project it onto various male figures, who thus became persecutors. In the patient's phantasies, they would punish him mercilessly for his own unmitigated primitive hostility.

I shall describe briefly another example of the structure of latent psychosis—the analytic history of the patient Michael whom I mentioned previously. He was a medical student who originally sought analytic treatment for the severe anxiety and panic which he developed at school. Clinically, he impressed me as anxiety hysteria with some latent homosexuality, a clinical impression which was confirmed by the projective technique. The patient made considerable improvement and was sent back to his school, which was in another city; it was not until the second stretch of analysis that the latent psychosis became manifest and overshadowed the neurotic symptomatology. Ideas of reference and of influence emerged at first as transference reactions and then became more generalized.

A deeply repressed and split-off masochistic pattern proved the nuclear element of this psychotic core. It could be traced back to an early game he used to play with his younger brother. When they were wrestling, he used to allow the little boy to win, imagining the pleasure it must give him to be on top. This game had the aim of releasing Michael from the guilt aroused by his destructive impulses against his brother, impulses which originated in intense sibling rivalry; thus he could hope to be assured of his mother's love which he might otherwise have lost because of his hatred of his little brother.

"As a result of its deep significance for the ego, after a time the masochist game, as it were, slipped out of control and became a habitual pattern to be acted out on different levels, mostly in phantasy and with varied men. In his relation with his fellow students and teachers, he reactivated his masochistic attitude so as to have a basis for pleading for help from them. But then he was afraid of the humiliation that he might bring upon himself and tried to counteract it by being overaggressive and by magnifying his professional successes and, by and large, emphasizing his virility. A series of chain reactions developed in which he felt afraid of the hostility of other men who might be antagonized by his delusional grandeur which he tried to establish in phantasy and to act out timidly in reality. Thus his ideas of reference and of persecution developed in direction from his being an object of special homosexual attention and interest toward being a target of scorn and hostility. At the same time, men, instead of being his friends and prospective protectors and helpers, became his enemies ready to jump at him and to humiliate, rape and castrate him. (I omit the important contribution made to this entire constellation by the inverted Oedipus complex.) Anal symptoms, which occurred at times of intense social anxiety, expressed most vividly his passive homosexual wishes. In his dreams and phantasies, both parents used to appear as powerful magic creatures who had set their minds on keeping him in complete dependence. His mother apeared in the guise of a witch who feeds her child only to devour it with more gusto. The father, who once upon a time had been devalued by the mother, and accordingly dethroned by the little boy, regained his old magic omnipotence.

"At this stage of the analysis, in a dream Michael recapitulated and rediscovered one of his basic unconscious paranoid phantasies. It consisted in his wish to restore mother's penis, which could be accomplished only by his submitting to being raped by the father. The analysis of this dream aroused intense anxiety, feelings of dizziness and depersonalization."[10]

There is hardly any need to multiply these examples. This and similar observations led me to the conclusion that the latent homosexual constellation is a constant and most significant element of latent schizophrenia. This constellation centers around a primitive maternal identification which, by virtue of splitting, remains isolated from the rest of the ego field. Various defense mechanisms are put in action in order to build up the counter-cathexis necessary for maintaining the dissociation of the passive, maternal, feminine sector of the ego field. Among these defensive measures of the ego, we may detect narcissistic withdrawal, secondary hostility and bouts of active homosexuality. Owing to the dissociation of the passive segment of the ego field, the rest of the ego is able to develop a deceptively "normal," seemingly realistic and even pseudo-masculine behavior while passivity, masochism and the megalomania of primary narcissism remain confined to the dissociated segment of the ego. This façade may be maintained until the moment when, due to some precipitating event, a breakdown of ego defenses reveals a crack in the total ego structure and results in a manifest psychosis.

Psychoanalytic observations of schizophrenics subjected to insulin shock therapy provide another opportunity for an understanding of the role of latent homosexuality in the origin of paranoid schizophrenia. In particular, these observations illustrate the important role played by the homosexual disappointment and the homosexual panic. The cathartic discharge provoked by the insulin coma creates a release of repressed libidinal impulses. The ambivalent homosexual attitude becomes split into its two components, with the positive one invested ideally in the transference reaction and thus accessible to analytic interpretations and working through.*

Psychoanalytic investigations have demonstrated the affinity between homosexuality and the schizophrenic break. In certain complex cases of latent homosexuality, the counter-cathexis, built by the ego in order to maintain the dissociation of the psychotic core from the rest of the ego, is so precarious that the psychotic invasion occurs, as it were, spontaneously and periodically. In such cases, the weakness of ego boundaries allows an intermittent release of internalized images which become projected onto various persons. The rapid shifting from passivity to activity and vice versa enables the individual to act out both attitudes, successively as well as simultaneously, and to play varied roles, according to his multiple identifications. Since his ego remains fixated in the stage of early narcissism, he is compelled to substitute homosexual acts for consistent and successful dealing with reality; in addition to libidinal gratification, the former offers the advantage of being invested heavily with magic omnipotence.

Elsewhere I have described at some length this type of patient.[11] His psychosexual development could be described as proceeding in four phases of successive internalization and externalization. Having been frequently subjected to anal stimulation by his mother through enemas and insertions of the thermometer, he proceeded to autoerotic play in which he applied similar stimulation to himself. This phase was followed by one of externalization in which he continued the same kind of play but with other boys as partners, and in his own role, frequently shifting from activity to passivity and vice versa.

* For a detailed description see my *Psychotherapy of Psychosis*, 180-187.

In a still further development, the play became internalized again, his father and older boys assuming various roles in his phantasies. Finally in the last stage of externalization, he acted out his phantasies—mostly with young sailors.

The kinship between schizophrenia and homosexuality is based on certain characteristics of ego formation. In my study of the ego of homosexuals, I have shown that the ego weakness characteristic of them is related to the ego weakness characteristic of schizophrenics. I came to the following conclusion: "The homosexual does not pursue the union with the woman, since, in its deep core, his ego has never separated from her. For the same reason, his ego has never really abandoned his prenatal narcissism and he has never acquired the feeling of virility. As a final consequence, he has never really been born into the society of men. Like the future paranoid, his ego has acquired a deep split. It has split off its primitive stage, what I have called the primitive superego, which has never come to grasp reality. Neither has it ever been able to accept any frustration. It has dealt with the latter by introjecting the maternal imago and trying to perpetuate possession through identification. It eternally pursues the phantom of its own and the father's masculinity by carrying within it the maternal image. In reality, it is bound to protect its deep narcissism. Its functioning is, in very truth, based on archaic constitution and primitive mental mechanisms,"[12] a formulation expressed by Freud as early as his *Three Contributions to the Theory of Sex*. Exaggerated narcissistic cathexis is a common characteristic of the ego of the homosexual and of the ego of schizophrenics. Fluidity of ego boundaries accounts for phenomena which are common to both groups of individuals.

A different point of view concerning the relationship between homosexuality and paranoia has been developed by Melanie

Klein and her disciples, most explicitly in a recent study by Rosenfeld. Melanie Klein believes in the so-called paranoid position in early infancy. Homosexuality, she feels, develops as a mechanism of defense against the ideas of persecution.[13] Rosenfeld has described three cases: of these, one was a manifest, another a latent homosexual; both developed paranoia when the defensive function of their homosexuality failed. In both, too, homosexuality was related to an idealized paternal figure, the idealization being used to deny the existence of the persecutor. In a third case, manifest homosexuality of a non-psychotic type covered up severe hidden paranoid anxiety.[14]

Rosenfeld thinks that the origin of the mechanism of projective identification lies in the earliest infantile impulses of forcing the self into the mother. He suggests that it is fixation on this early level that may be responsible for the frequent combination of both paranoia and homosexuality. Despite the great interest of this clinical material, I find it difficult to accept his conclusions; neither theoretically nor clinically have I been convinced that the idea of an infantile paranoid position is valid.

Elements of homosexuality may be included in the structure of various forms of depression. They are evident in some cases of paranoid depressive reaction in the period of involution. Here the paranoid ideas not infrequently represent a projection of long-repressed homosexual fantasies; the patient either feels directly accused of homosexual acts or threatened by persecutors who want to assault him, make him into a male (or female, as the case may be) prostitute, etc.

According to psychoanalytic insight, the characteristic essential mechanism of the melancholic depression lies in introjection. Occasionally, however, projective mechanisms come into action; in that case, paranoid trends may be added to the picture of a so-called pure depression. Prevalence of such symptomatology may be indicative of the importance of schizophrenic elements in the structure of psychosis. To be sure, some germ of paranoid delusion can be observed in almost every depression of long duration. This was already recorded by that great expert on melancholia, Robert Burton: "The melancholy are always aggressive. They cannot speak but they must bite. But they are unaware of their own aggression and feel attacked instead. As they that drink wine think all runs around when it is in their own brain."[15]

Obviously, any homosexual person may develop a depression. In manifest homosexuality, this may occur under a variety of conditions. Disappointment in or loss of a love-object is a common one. So is that of the individual aware of his inversion but not practicing it because he is restrained by ethical or religious motives. Under certain circumstances, it may even be possible that a young person is preconsciously or even consciously aware of his sexual deviation but tries to deny it to himself, usually under the impact of horror aroused by a feeling of guilt. In these cases, which naturally have become less and less frequent due to the progress of general enlightenment, we have the rare opportunity of relieving an individual from depression by means of a simple and thorough explanation. It will depend upon a variety of circumstances whether we should then attempt to correct the inversion by means of analytic therapy.

We need more detailed psychoanalytic observations to understand the role of latent homosexuality in the structure of depression. Genetically, we may distinguish two main layers of dynamic connection—the first related to the early preOedipal, so-called primal depression, the second bearing on the special outcome of the Oedipal conflict.

The primal depression in the small child, as it has been described by Abraham, is the result of an early disappointment. If this even is focused on the parent of the opposite sex, it becomes natural for the child to turn for consolation to the parent of the same sex. When let down in turn by the latter, the child experiences what has been called homosexual disappointment. The role of such early disappointments in originating depression has been more recently studied by Jacobson.[16]

The second genetic layer, the Oedipal conflict, results in turning the child's ego toward passive submission to the parent of the opposite sex. Thus the boy identifies with the mother and wants to receive love from his father at the price of emasculation. The girl turns in a similar way toward the mother whom she may endow with masculine attributes. Naturally, previous pre-Oedipal and pregenital fixations play a decisive role in predisposing to such an outcome of the Oedipal conflict.

It should be clear that this constellation may arise on the basis of various clinical configurations, among others on the basis of active or latent homosexuality. However, an additional disappointment in the secondary homosexual object choice may be considered an important factor in the development of depression at some later age.

Analysis of such patients frequently reveals a core of considerable ego weakness which is covered up by a façade of obsessive compulsive symptomatology and various ego defenses embedded in the character structure. Aggression, though partially sublimated, remains on a primitive level and is consequently equated by the superego with barbaric destruction. Accordingly, when the life situation calls for decisive action, this is experienced as a dangerous emergency, threatening the ego with retaliation from the superego and its parental counterpart. Consequently, the ego turns to the passive feminine and masochistic position, where, instead of being a source of action, it makes itself into an object of action coming from others. A persistent though entirely unconscious pursuit of this attitude must result in increasing inhibition which, in turn, checks normal human activities. The inhibition serves a number of objectives. It checks destructive impulses, prevents the unfolding of active homosexuality and gratifies the unconscious wish for a passive and masochistically feminine gratification.

In patients of both sexes, the passive wish turns toward both parents. In males, the homosexual element is linked with the father and/or with the older brother while the mother is seen ambivalently in her pre-Oedipal as well as Oedipal aspect. From the pre-Oedipal aspect, she appears as an object of anaclitic love and as the generous breast but, at the same time, as a source of deprivation and domineering aggression. From the Oedipal aspect, she is not only the object of love but also carries over the pre-Oedipal aggressive implications and seems to side with the father in frustrating the libidinal objectives of her little son. With obvious changes, this constellation may be applied to the female patient. Here both the maternal and the paternal superego seem to conspire in frustrating all attempts at activity. The mother is well fitted to become the object of passive anaclitic and aggressively demanding love. The homosexual object-choice, superimposed on this original attitude, is designed to supersede and bypass the dangerous Oedipal situation.

In a twenty-two-year-old college student, whom I described elsewhere in some detail, the general and especially the intellectual inhibition served the purpose of passive submission to the father and, in terms of mental structure, of the surrender of the ego to the punishing superego.

The severe malancholic depression of this patient developed

in a somewhat Hamlet-like situation after his mother had decided to divorce his father, who had been unfaithful to her for a long time, without any pretense at discretion. All the patient's conflicts became dramatically sharpened when he was suddenly called to the bedside of the father, who, by that time, had already left his home. The father had been wounded by his mistress and the patient was supposed to act in behalf of both parents.

Like the Danish prince, the patient was now called upon to assume his father's role in the family situation. However, this responsibility mobilized his unresolved Oedipal conflict and, owing to castration fear, made him regress to the never abandoned and only partly repressed passive feminine position. One of the solutions of the Oedipal situation which had been attempted by the little boy and never totally abandoned was turning toward his father in passive submission and ardent clinging. Instead of carrying out a successful Oedipal rebellion, he had remained passionately attached to the father. But more than that, threatened as he was by his own hostility and the anticipated retalition of the father, he had felt compelled to preserve the paternal image within himself as an indispensable core of strength and virility. To give this up, to separate himself from the introjected image, would mean to resign himself to utter weakness.

The patient's severe melancholic inhibition (which eventually yielded completely to psychoanalysis) was also, at its core, a manifestation of his deep anality. Between the ages of five and seven, he suffered from severe constipation and was often punished for not doing his duty. Being kept at home was the punishment he resented most; for a while, his daily activities seemed regulated by the function of his intestines. Since that time, he consistently resented all "duties" and every rigid time schedule. It became clear that, in maintaining his melancholic inhibition, the patient was refusing to produce and, consequently, was punishing himself by refusing to leave home. At the same time, he was continuing and increasing his inhibition while resisting all external pressure and refusing to submit to a generally accepted schedule.

The personality structure of drug addicts shows, in many instances, elements of latent or manifest homosexuality. By and large, the link between this defect and addiction may be described schematically in two contrasting ways. In one group, we deal with individuals whose egos, owing to various structural defects and passive fixations and identifications, could not properly integrate their aggressive drives. The latter thus remained on a primitive level, without undergoing the usual process of neutralization and sublimation. However, gratification of such primitive aggressive drives cannot easily be obtained in any socially acceptable setting. Consequently, one of the ways open to individuals of this type leads to criminality. The other way compels them to seek means of alleviating the frustrations which inevitably result from their inability to satisfy primitive narcissistic and aggressive goals. It is this latter way which may lead to addiction. This point of view also makes clear the dynamic reasons for the frequent combination of addiction and certain forms of criminality.

The role of homosexuality in this group may be confined to repressed active homosexual impulses; on the other hand, manifest homosexual activity may dominate the picture. Then homosexual acts provide the opportunity not only for libidinal gratification but also for a discharge of primitive aggression. Every act of homosexual "conquest" may be experienced by the ego as a denial of its inherent weakness and a reassertion and reaffirmation of pseudo-masculinity.

In the second group of addicts, we see individuals with an ego core characterized by utter passivity, with little room left for aggression on any level. According to various dynamic and external circumstances, they may either manifest their latent homosexuality by passively submitting to the pressure of seduction by aggressive drug addicts or else succumb to homosexual seduction and combine it with addiction, usually practiced together with their sexual partners.

The dynamic factors responsible for the personality of the drug addict may become more apparent in the course of deepening addiction. This holds true especially for the passive submissive type. As to the aggressive paranoid group, the drug may temporarily cover up their basic psychopathology. However, their general irritability—connected with the difficulties they meet in their efforts to obtain increasing amounts of the drug—must in the long run activate the paranoid aggressive structure. In such individuals, withdrawal may produce a complex psychotic picture with evidence of paranoid elements. Among my own patients of this type, I observed symptoms of conversion hysteria and hallucinations reminiscent of delirium tremens but with preserved orientation in time and space. Recognition of environment was disturbed by delusions in which projection of the aggressive and homoerotic core could be clearly observed. Thus one of these patients was convinced that he was being transferred to the female ward in order to humiliate him before the physicians, as though they wanted to "change him into a woman." He also complained of being sexually aroused by contact with the physician's leg.[17]

The homosexual deviation in cocaine addicts was first described by Hartmann in extensive clinical studies.[18]

In certain cases, addiction is but the manifestation of a latent or circumscribed psychosis. In an observation of Benedek, the patient wanted to destroy her feminine body which she hated. This wish had emerged in her adolescence. She drank heavily and stuffed herself with large quantities of food. The drive toward bodily self-destruction served as a defense against repressed homosexuality. In her wish to destroy her feminine ego, she was also trying to destroy her mother with whom she identified herself on the oral level. The defensive struggle against this identification led to paranoid hatred of women.[19]

In this context, I would like to mention briefly my own observation of compulsive bulimia in a schizophrenic girl. Here analysis demonstrated clearly that the compulsive eating served the purpose of re-establishing the original oral identification with her mother; at the same time, it meant the destruction of her feminine loveliness, since it transformed her into a shapeless mass of flesh and fat. In this way, the patient was defending herself desperately not only against any heterosexual potentialities but, on a deeper level, against the narcissistic-homosexual love for the mother and her substitutes. The voice of her phantasy lover, that is, of her father, threatened to kill her unless she continued to stuff herself with food. Compulsive hair-pulling was another means of destroying her femininity and forcing her into continued dependence on her parents. Her psychotic imagery expressed the split in her homosexual attitude. She was being threatened by her "beautiful" mother holding a sword while, at the same time, she was yearning for the lovely female figures of her own phantasy.

In my observations of neurotic obesity, I became aware of the role played by repressed homosexuality in my predominantly female patients. One of them, in addition to compulsive overeating, developed during analysis addiction to benzedrine which led her to take, in complete secrecy, immense quantities of the drug. She then displayed a transient paranoid psychosis in which the analyst became her chief persecutor with evil sexual intentions. The homosexual element could easily be detected in this heterosexually oriented delusional formation.

One of the few male patients of this series was an active homosexual given especially to oral practices. Food meant strength to him and overeating was a manifestation of his wish to strengthen his weak ego, since, as he put it: "One has more security when one has the stomach full." In the early history of this patient, severe and continuous disappointments in his father led to a regressive overfixation on and identification with his mother. His compulsive homosexuality expressed his search for a father and was a means of replenishing his weak and depleted ego. With the progress of analysis, he experienced changes in his mental and somatic ego feeling. He stopped overeating and, with his increased interest in work, felt less fatigued and sleepy. Eventually, after a complete change in his sexual attitude, he lost altogether his compulsive need for food.

Among my women patients who were addicts, denial of femininity was a prominent feature; it manifested itself by amenorrhea and avoidance of feminine grace and apparel. In homosexual episodes, patients played the aggressive masculine role. In their heterosexual relations, they showed complete vaginal anaesthesia and, as one of my patients put it: they did not "discover" their vagina until a fairly advanced stage of analysis. It is in keeping with this attitude that, to their unconscious, food had also the symbolic meaning of the paternal phallus which they wanted to incorporate and thus to keep forever.[20]

Finally, we have to consider the role of homosexuality in that most popular and best-known form of addiction, alcoholism. Both superficial and clinical observation concur in stressing the predominance of certain homosexual trends in alcoholics. Here belong such trends as the importance of drinking in common, in certain male group activities, the particular kind of conviviality and fraternization displayed by the drinker and, on the defensive side, the manifestation of paranoid tendencies with their further psychotic elaboration.

A recent psychological study of latent homosexuality in alcoholism is rather skeptical about the connection. Botwinick and Machower tested the "normality" of their alcoholic subjects with regard to their sexual interest pattern. They arrived at the conclusion that "insofar as the test used in this measures homosexuality, latent or otherwise, homosexuality cannot be an essential factor in alcoholism, although it may play a dynamic role in individual cases."[21]

However, psychoanalytic authors, by and large, have agreed on the importance of latent homosexuality in the dynamics of alcoholism. Theoretically, this could be expected in view of such trends as orality and narcissism—trends which certainly are shared in common by the alcoholic and the homosexual. Clinically, we are impressed by the fact that alcoholism appears as one of the significant patterns of behavior in individuals with a weak ego structure. A similar ego structure is found in most homosexuals, latent as well as manifest. Clinical observations of non-psychotic and psychotic alcoholics point to trends which may be considered as characteristic—though certainly not specific—of latent homosexuality, such trends as impotence, suspiciousness and jealousy.

The analytic insight into the personality structure of many alcoholics shows that they are characterized by narcissism and orality. They are individuals in whom difficult family constellations were responsible for oral frustrations in early childhood. Oral fixations resulted in a personality structure similar to the depressive personality with a low frustration tolerance.

As a result of this early development, male individuals tend to turn away from the frustrating mother to the father; that is, they substitute an inverted for the positive Oedipal constellation. In this way, the basis is laid for future homosexuality.

Abraham was the first to recognize the significance of latent homosexuality in the etiology of alcohol addiction. He spoke of men turning to alcohol as a means of gaining an increased feeling of manliness and of flattering their complex of masculinity. He drew attention to characteristic mannerisms of alcoholics and to special drinking customs among such groups as university students—all of them bearing typical latent homosexual characteristics. He also drew an interesting comparison between the structure of alcoholics and perverts.[22] Juliusburger discussed the relation of homosexuality to inebriety and pointed out that periodic stages of anxiety may result from strong latent homosexual impulses. According to his observations, dipsomania is a manifestation of such unconscious homosexual drives, periodically breaking through the barrier of repression. Anxiety which manifests itself at the beginning of a dipsomanic attack arises under the impact of an unconscious homosexual wish; in our modern terminology, we would describe it as a reaction of the ego to the breaking through of the id impulses.[23] In some of my own observations, I found a similar pattern— with the emphasis put on seeking a rapprochement with other men as a substitute for a deficiency in the early relationship to the father.

Weyl (1926, 1944), who has made an extensive study of alcoholism and has developed some original ideas on the subject, stressed the role of homosexuality and the destruction of homosexual sublimations. The latter become replaced by superficial sociability and anal-sadistic regression. Weyl also emphasized the obsessive character of drinking ceremonies and the symbolic meaning in the ingestion of alcohol, the intoxicant representing both parental figures. In his hypothesis, group drinking has the symbolic meaning of a totem feast and therefore represents the reciprocal identification of the male group. "The excessive use of alcohol makes it possible to realize in a phantastic subjective way, the primitive solution of the Oedipus complex."[24]

Knight observed, in his alcoholic patients, a conscious or almost conscious fear of being regarded as feminine. They showed impotence and *ejaculatio praecox* and a typical dichotomy in their love and sex life.[25] I can also confirm his observation that women with a strong homosexual component resort to drinking as a means of identifying and competing with men.

In view of the genetic and dynamic factors which alcoholism and perversion have in common, their clinical coexistence is understandable and to be expected. The common background is especially striking in patients where both the addiction to alcohol and active homosexuality are manifestations of a slowly progressing and insidious schizophrenic process. We shall speak later of clinical developments which may arise with this background.

In another group of patients, inebriety serves the objective of helping them to overcome whatever inhibitions they may have toward active gratification of their homosexual impulses. Here alcohol not only fulfills its classic role as a dissolvent of the superego but is used as such quite consciously and deliberately. Some patients have to get drunk because only then are they able to master enough courage to engage in the search for a homosexual partner; others, in order to overcome the apprehension they feel in passively submitting to the aggression of anal penetration.

The deliberate use of alcohol for these purposes becomes particularly apparent when a patient—who in his psychoanalysis has made enough progress to stop homosexual acting out—gets himself intoxicated and reverts to his old practices; he does it every so often after having discussed the problem with his analyst and made solemn promises not to touch a drink during this delicate period in his analysis.

The rich variety of clinical developments which arise from the common background of insidious schizophrenia, alcoholism and perversion is well known to descriptive psychiatry. From the analytic point of view, the main distinction consists, perhaps, in the attitude of the ego toward perversion. We observe patients whose ego accepts homosexuality as a drive as well as a gratification. Here perversion may become more or less integrated into the general pattern of living, without causing any other reaction than, possibly, anxiety based on a good appraisal of reality. Obviously, it is only natural that a passive young man who gets intoxicated and then seeks out tough, aggressive men in order to submit to their anal aggression, should fear the consequences of these encounters. A patient of this type admitted that he had been beaten up and robbed —but "only" twice in the course of four years of intense homosexual activity. The patient accepted both his masochism and his homosexuality. In his phantasies, he saw himself embraced and anally penetrated by a strong, tough man. When he got drunk, he felt this urge with the greatest intensity and sought its gratfication in reality. He felt neither shame nor compunction nor did he suffer from anything even remotely approaching ideas of reference.

In sharp contrast with such acceptance by the ego, we observe patients who engage in an unremitting struggle with their homosexual drive. The continuous character of this defensive battle bears testimony to the pressure of the drive and to the inadequacy of the ego to cope with it. Under these circumstances, it is to be excepted that, despite the defensive system built up by the ego, the drive may break through time and again. We then obtain the picture of a paranoid development with the homosexual drive breaking through, either in a direct or an only slightly disguised form. In such cases, the alcohol serves to facilitate the eruption and even the gratification of the ego-alien perverse drive.

In the least complicated alcoholic psychosis, alcoholic delirium, we may observe elements of slightly disguised heterosexuality or homosexuality. Tausk pointed out, as far back as 1915, the analogy of structure between the typical occupational delirium and the occupational dream. He interpreted alcoholic delirium as the expression of sexual excitement in patients who are impotent and, at the same time, inhibited by their narcissism and homosexuality. The saloon, according to him, "replaces the woman; at the same time, it is an attempt to sublimate their homosexuality."[26]

The most complete, to my knowledge, analysis of a case of delirium tremens was published in 1926 by Kielholz. The analysis confirmed his former findings concerning the importance of the homosexual component in alcoholics. Clear homosexual and sadomasochistic tendencies in the patient were instrumental in shaping frightening hallucinations of individuals who were, for the most part, objects of his emotional and libidinal attitudes. Some of these fancied attacks on the patient had the characteristics of direct homosexual aggression. Kielholz pointed out the connection between the mass character of animal hallucinations and the deep libidinal links binding the drinker to his male drinking friends.[27]

The threatening and castrating character of the hallucinations in alcoholic delirium was the object of a special study by Bromberg and Schilder. They described the dismembering tendency of these experiences which they found in the foreground of the clinical picture. The persecutors were chiefly other men—soldiers, drinking companions and the like. The choice of these persons was motivated by latent homosexual tendencies.[28]

Paranoid elements may already appear in the acute stages of so-called alcoholic hallucinosis. Voices accuse the patient of various misdeeds, among them not infrequently homosexual activities, and threaten him with a punishment which often amounts to symbolic or undisguised rape and castration.

In further clinical development, both the delirium and the hallucinosis may evolve into a chronic paranoid psychosis. It is generally believed that, in such cases, alcoholism was the manifestation of a latent or otherwise not recognized schizophrenia. It is easy to recognize typical defense mechanisms, used by the ego in its struggle against the breaking through of homosexuality, in the ideas of jealousy. They are a classic feature in many a chronic alcoholic and reach their peak in a paranoid psychosis.

The struggle against homosexuality may be covered up by the ego in various ways so that, in certain cases, we may see in succession a whole gamut of defense mechanisms. Obsessive-compulsive symptomatology may be followed by paranoid episodes until, finally, aggressive homosexuality may break through under the impact of alcoholic intoxication. In such patients, inebriety assumes the characteristics of so-called pathological intoxication, with outbursts of violent aggression and homosexual acts or, at least, overt impulses and phantasies.

In a patient under my observation, these episodes clearly amounted to what may be described as a self-induced psychosis. In his early childhood, he was exposed to an unusual amount of aggression from both parents. His mother, full of hostility and possessed of a violent temper, used to tell the children that their father would kill them if he ever found out about their various transgressions. These included going to church, since the mother was a devout Catholic while the father belonged to a different creed. After absorbing this great dose of aggression, the patient naturally identified masculinity with savage brutality and isolated both from the rest of his ego. Oral identification with the mother and an inverted Oedipal constellation, with emphasis on femininity and passivity, were a natural result of this development. There was a great fear of the father, that is, of his incorporated and isolated aggression. Since the father was described by the mother as likely to become insane with rage and then capable of homicide, the patient had developed an intense fear of his father, of other men and of insanity. His passive and mostly latent homosexuality served the purpose of placating the dangerous father and his substitutes and of neutralizing his own aggressive virility.

In fighting off his Oedipal sexuality, he had experienced intense castration fear in connection with Oedipally colored masturbation. Accordingly, after turning passively toward his father, he connected strong orgastic sensations with anal masturbation and with his passive feminine constellation. In keeping with this development, passive homosexual phantasies would crop up whenever he was close to any real professional or heterosexual attainment.

In his first line of defensive struggle against passive homosexual impulses, he developed a few obsessive ideas in which he progressed from a slightly disguised fear of being anally assaulted to the fear of himself assaulting first men and, eventually, women. In these regressive formations, sexuality assumed a more and more aggressive character until his obsessive ideas became centered around the fear of hurting his former wife, his woman friend and, most insistently, his own beloved little son. The latter went to live with his mother after the patient and his wife had separated and, eventually, came to be the main object of his father's obsessive solicitude.

It soon became clear that the little boy represented his own self; consequently, he became the main object of the patient's narcissistic and destructive impulses. Thus, in his unconscious wish to hurt him and in his conscious love and obsessively exaggerated solicitude, the patient was in reality expressing his own narcissistically redirected love and hatred. While this was one of the channels for his primitive instinctual constellations, they could not be satisfied with this outlet alone and were manifesting themselves in various homosexual phantasies and in his thrusts toward heterosexuality.

Yet all his attempts at forming permanent object relations were thwarted by powerful aggressive and narcissistic impulses. He explained that he felt harassed by his little boy and his future wife, the woman friend, because he felt responsible for their every move and emotion in addition to their well-being. It became clear to him that the reason for this oversolicitousness was his complete identification with them; the identification went so far that he actually became *they*: he was the little boy as well as the woman. It was because of this "intertwining," this lack of any distance from the object, that he could not establish a true love relationship. As a defense against the wish for such absolute identification, he was maintaining aggressive obsessive thoughts directed against his two main love-objects. In addition, in defense against his narcissistic and masochistic love for the woman, he was maintaining an attitude of compulsive promiscuity. It became clear to him that his complete lack of responsibility in the love relationship was the most effective defense against his unconscious wish for "absolute" responsibility—that is, for a complete fusion with the woman. In the last analysis, this proved to be his defense against his infantile wish to be devoured by the substitute mother.

Drinking was started by the patient at an early age as a part of his identification with two older, aggressive and intensely promiscuous brothers whom he idolized. In this way he laid down the foundation which led him to resort to alcohol as a way of temporarily breaking the shackles of repression and isolation, maintained by a strict and punitive superego. In his youth, the patient had become involved in an automobile accident in which one of the two passengers was killed. The other passenger was himself, the victim his cousin and dear companion. It had never been established which of the two men—both were intoxicated—had been at the wheel. This tragic event provided the patient with a good justification for his obsessive fear of insanity and homicide.

Yet it was precisely the release of uncontrollable impulses which he was seeking in his bouts of dipsomania. He compared himself, in his drinking spells, with a gangster felling a policeman with a blow. He could then freely express his violent aggression; once he almost strangled his woman companion and knocked down his best friend when the latter tried to interfere.

He could also give way freely to his homosexual phantasies and, occasionally, at least prior to his analysis, could fulfill them. At the same time, he was trying to emancipate himself from the maternal image by destroying the relationship with his woman friend by his irresponsible promiscuity.

This patient used to experience intense sexual and even orgastic feelings shortly before and after the peak of intoxication. Then, and only then, did he feel that he could allow himself full sexual pleasure; otherwise it seemed to him fraught with danger and similar, in the terror it awoke, to what he had experienced during his childhood and adolescent masturbation. Since then, he had become afraid of what he called automatic orgasm which would call for castration as punishment (he had experienced a feeling of estrangement in his hands) and which, as we remember, he had also equated with insanity.

Resorting to alcohol allowed him a full realization of his bisexuality: he felt, he said, both like a man and like a woman; that is, then and only then was he permitted full identification with his both loved and hated, desired and feared parents. At the same time, in his outbursts of rage, he could potentially destroy his parents in the person of his friends and of other even casually met male figures, as well as in the person of his beloved. As a matter of fact, he was obviously trying to destroy himself; he used to resort to drinking bouts on the verge of some significant attainment in his professional career, in his love life and, last but not least, in his analysis.

The deep connection between his homosexuality, his obsessive ideas and his self-induced alcoholic psychosis became completely clear after we realized that, since his earliest childhood, the patient had lived in suspense, awaiting the realization of violence, inevitably supposed to erupt from his father. He was anticipating it by identification in his obsessive thinking while, in his dipsomanic spells, he was actually acting it out so as finally to get the longed-for liberation. His homosexual impulses, however, the active as well as the predominantly passive masochistic ones, served the purpose of protecting him against the looming horror of paternal and, to a lesser extent, maternal aggression.

While these were the deep unconscious goals of the dipsomanic attacks, on the surface they were easily explained by the typical rationalizations which, to him and to his friends, seemed not without validity. It was at such times, obviously, that he could overcome his timidity and was enabled to establish friendly relations both with persons in authority and casually met bar companions. Moreover, he could shake off the fetters of his love relation and pending marriage by feeling free to approach any women who attracted his attention.

It has seemed to me that this fragment of a case history might serve as a fitting conclusion to my discussion. It illustrates the original as well as the ego defensive character of homosexual impulses, their connection with narcissism and early ego formation, and some of the many clinical elaborations which they undergo in the course of the development and various struggles of the ego.

REFERENCES

1 For references to older bibliography see:
   Humbert, P. *Homosexualité et Psychopathies*. Paris, 1935.

2 Zilboorg, G. *A History of Medical Psychology*. New York, 1941.

3 Freud, Sigmund. "Psychoanalytic Notes upon an Autobiographical Account of a Case of Paranoia." *Coll. Papers*, Vol. III. London, 1924.

   ———. "Certain Neurotic Mechanisms in Jealousy, Paranoia and Homosexuality." *Coll. Papers*, Vol. II. London, 1924.

————. "A Case of Paranoia Running Counter to the Psychoanalytical Theory of the Disease." *Coll. Papers*, Vol. II. London, 1924.

4 Ferenczi, S. "On the Part Played by Homosexuality in the Pathogenesis of Paranoia." *Sex in Psychoanalysis*. New York, 1950.

————. "Some Clinical Observations on Paranoia and Paraphrenia." *Ibid.*

5 Bak, R. "Masochism in Paranoia." *Psychoanalytic Quarterly*, Vol. XV, 1946.

6 MacAlpine, J., and Hunter, R. A. "The Schreber Case." *Psychoanalytic Quarterly*, Vol. XXII, 1953.

7 Nunberg, H. "On the Catatonic Attack." *International Zeitschrift für Psychoanalyse*, Vol. VI, 1920.

————. "Libidinal Conflict in Schizophrenia." *Ibid.*, Vol. VII, 1921. (Both in *Practice and Theory of Psychoanalysis*. New York, 1948.)

8 Bychowski, G. "A Case of Oral Delusions of Persecution." *International Journal of Psychoanalysis*, Vol. XI, 1930.

9 ————. "Problems of Latent Psychosis." *Journal of the American Psychoanalytic Association*, Vol. I, 1953.

10 ————. *Psychotherapy of Psychosis*. New York, 1952.

11 ————. "The Structure of Homosexual Acting Out." *Psychoanalytic Quarterly*, Vol. XXIII, 1954.

12 ————. "The Ego of Homosexuals." *International Journal of Psychoanalysis*, Vol. XXVI, 1945.

13 Klein, M. "Notes on Some Schizoid Mechanisms." *International Journal of Psychoanalysis*, Vol. XXVII, 1946.

14 Rosenfeld, H. "Remarks on the Relation of Male Homosexuality to Paranoia, Paranoid Anxiety and Narcissism." *International Journal of Psychoanalysis*, Vol. XXX, 1949.

15 Burton, Robert. *The Anatomy of Melancholy* (quoted in *The Psychiatry of Robert Burton* by Bergen Evans. New York, 1944.).

16 Jacobson, E. "Depression—the Oedipus Complex in the Development of Depressive Mechanisms." *Psychoanalytic Quarterly*, Vol. XII, 1943.

————. "The Effect of Disappointment on Ego and Superego Formation in Normal and Depressive Development." *Psychoanalytic Review*, Vol. XXXIII, 1946.

17   Bychowski, G. "Sur les Troubles Nerveux et Psychiques de la Démorphinisation" (in Polish, with French Summary, in a volume to the Honor of E. Flatau). Warsaw, 1929.

18   Hartmann, H. "Cocainismus und Homosexualität." *Zeitschrift für die gesamte Neurologie und Psychiatrie*, Vol. XCV, 1925.

————. "Cocainismus und Homosexualität." *Deutsche Medizinische Wochenschrift*, 1928.

19   Benedek, T. "Dominant Ideas and Their Relation to Morbid Cravings." *International Journal of Psychoanalysis*, Vol. XVII, 1936.

20   Bychowski, G. "On Neurotic Obesity." *Psychoanalytic Review*, Vol. XXXVII, 1950.

21   Botwinick, J., and Machover, S. "Psychometric Examination of Latent Homosexuality in Alcoholism." *Quarterly Journal of Studies in Alcohol*, Vol. 12, 1951.

22   Abraham, K. "The Psychological Relation between Sexuality and Alcoholism." *Selected Papers*. London, 1927.

23   Juliusberger, O. "Beitrag zur Psychologie der Sogenannten Dipsomanie." *Centralblatt für Psychoanalyse*, Vol. II, 1912.

24   Weyl, S. "Zur Psychologie der Alcoholismus." *Internationale Zeitschrift für Psychoanalyse*, Vol. XIII, 1927. (Convention paper)

————. "Psychoanalytic Therapy of Problem Drinkers." *Quarterly Journal of Studies in Alcohol*, Vol. V, 1944.

25   Knight, R. "Zur Dynamik und Therapie des chronishcen Alkoholismus." *Internationale Zeitschrift für Psychoanalyse*, Vol. XXIII, 1937.

26   Tausk, V. "Zur Psychologie des alkoholischen Beschäftigungsdelirium." *Internationale Zeitschrift für Psychoanalyse*, Vol. III, 1915.

27   Kielholz, A. "Analyse-versuch bei Delirium Tremens."
     Internationale Zeitschrift für Psychoanalyse, Vol. XII,
     1926.

28   Bromberg, W., and Schilder, P. "Psychological Considera-
     tions in Alcoholic Hallucinations." *International Journal
     of Psychoanalysis*, Vol. XIV, 1933.

A Developmental Theory
of Female Homosexuality

CATHERINE LILLIE BACON

Freud attempted to explain the universality of both conscious and unconscious homosexual and bisexual phantasies on the basis of a bisexual constitution. In discussing the psychosexual development of women, he expressed the opinion that their earliest attachment to the mother is a masculine one and that the little girl believes either that everyone is equipped with genitals like her own or that her genital is identified with the penis. It is not until the discovery of the penis, sometime between the ages of two to four, that girls, after going through a depressed phase of feeling that they have been castrated, gradually develop a positive Oedipus complex. Freud believed that girls turn away from their mothers in anger and disappointment at not having been given a masculine genital and that the Oedipus complex is founded on a tempestuous turning to the father in the hope of acquiring one. Only later, when this hope, too, is dissapointed, are they able to adopt a passive feminine attitude with the wish to have a baby by the father.

In opposition to Freud's views, at about the same time in England, Jones held that both homosexuality and bisexuality could be explained as due to the vicissitudes that occur during the development of the child. He felt that the little girl's attitude was primarily and biologically feminine and that penis envy occurred after a series of traumata. Thus the masculine protest in girls and feminine identification in boys were the result of neurotic new formations occurring because of disappointment and anxiety suffered during the Oedipal phase. He quoted Melanie Klein in showing that penis envy developed because of the little girl's need to protect herself against her mother as a result of conscious and unconscious Oedipal hostility. Horney also felt that the original orientation of the little girl was feminine and that penis envy was the result of a cultural situation, where the boy is preferred in the family, and also of the little girl's infantile envy at seeing someone else have something she does not have. In 1940, Rado attacked the theory of constitutional bisexuality, both on biological and psychological grounds, and again emphasized that perverse ways of gaining sexual gratification were the result of traumatic infantile experiences. The following will be an attempt to enlarge upon the thinking of this group who feel that homosexuality and bisexuality are developmental and not constitutional in origin.

I shall first attempt to reconstruct infantile development from the point of later pathology and then go on to show how traumatic situations arising in childhood can turn the little girl from the normal paths of feminine development.

The child starts out in life with relatively few reflex responses and the ability to learn by experience. As it develops, the instinct to be fed and loved and cared for becomes inextricably interwoven with the sexual instinct. The sexual drive in the young child is largely dependent in nature, since, before it can mature, it has to learn a great deal about sexual attitudes. In human beings, the knowledge of sexual techniques is not inherited but learned. The wish to be helped and to learn about sex frequently, in its symbolism, takes the same form as a child's wish for food. When the normal wish to learn about sex is interfered with, either by the parents' refusal, anger or withdrawal of love, my contention is that the normal instinct for heterosexual learning or sexual dependence may be turned from its true path into a perversion.

Both Lewin and Melanie Klein have postulated the earliest relationship of the infant with the mother as eating at the breast with phantasies of being eaten in return. Melaine Klein is inclined to view the relationship of the baby with the mother as primarily greedy and aggressive and states that the baby has frightening phantasies of being eaten up as a result of its greed. Lewin tends to emphasize the erotic nature of this relationship, postulating that, with these phantasies of eating and being eaten, both of which are pleasurable, the baby goes to sleep at the mother's breast. This relationship becomes threatening only when neurotic conflicts intervene.

I should like to draw attention to the fact that there is an added element in the eating and being eaten phantasy or rhythm in the mother-child relationship. After the baby has eaten at the breast, it frequently both urinates and/or defecates. This is a reflex reaction, since, in feeding, both the gastro-colic and the gastro-urethral reflexes are stimulated. In the earliest months of childhood, this stimulation usually occurs while eating or immediately afterward. So that, in the child's mind, eating and excreting become closely connected. The excretion and the changing of diapers are also part of its erotic relationship with the mother. While usually, in analytic literature, the baby is not considered to have any conflict with the mother over excretion in the first months of life, I have had some clinical evidence which indicates that mothers who dislike diapers and their odor handle babies coldly when changing them and already may cause some anxiety about the excretory part of the feeding act.

A clinical example illustrating this point is the following: Anne, a young mother in analysis with me, had let her son spend the weekend with her sister. When the child came home on Sunday evening, he expressed delight that his aunt had allowed him to choose his farewell meal in which the main dish was hamburger. Anne was filled with jealousy as she listened, and felt a choking sensation in her throat. That night she dreamed:

> "I was out on the street walking when I suddenly had a bowel movement. I was very embarrassed, but, as I turned to look at it, it changed into hamburger."

In the dreams of an adult, one naturally gets the maturer experiences along with the earlier, more primitive thinking. Obviously, Anne had wishes to be defiant and to be a prostitute (streetwalking) which came out in response to her angry jealousy of her sister. However, the more primitive thinking in the dream is the following: Anne realized that her older sister had given something to her child that was important to him. That made her consciously jealous and angry. However, she started to "swallow" this news in spite of her anger, i.e., she choked on it. The result was that, in the dream, she indicated to the child that she, too, could make hamburgers as her sister could. In this wish to compete with the sister, the gastro-colic reflex was also at work; having swallowed the information about hamburgers, she could reproduce it in the form of a stool. Anne had a tendency to feed her child "what was good for him" rather than what he wanted. She had, in reality, learned something from the child's pleasure in choosing his own food. This was reproduced in the dream along with a lot of hostility to her sister, and to me in the mother-transference.

It is because of dreams like Anne's that I postulate that anything learned may also be reacted to actively in a wish to emulate, which, in the small child, may be expressed by either anal or sexual impulses. This follows Freud's formulation that the child has a tendency to repeat actively any experience that is passively imposed on him. In other words, Anne had been forced to absorb the fact that her son had been fed what he wanted by her sister. She responded to it angrily, as she had responded to gaining knowledge about her parents' sexual relations as a child—which made her feel shut out and unloved. In the dream the next night, actively and in an excretory fashion, she played the same role as her sister, as well as caricaturing her mother's sexual role with her father (the streetwalking). It is quite important that the competition with the sister is an excretory one. Certainly, the manifest content of the dream indicates that feces are good to eat.

I am introducing a term, "the infantile metabolic phantasy," to indicate the sum total of infantile phantasies not only only those centering on the actual problem of the physiological metabolic process (eating, digestion, withholding and excretion) —but also those which have to do with learning, psychological digestion and resultant active behavior. These phantasies may later be transferred to the analyst and studied as a "metabolic transference."

As will be seen from the dream given above, the metabolic process can be a complex one. In this dream, Anne "learns" about hamburgers and becomes angry and jealous. She reproduces hamburgers for her son, but she also wishes to hurt the sister. She relates what her son told her to what she learned in childhood about her parents' sexual life. In this dream, we get a split in the response to this introject. She wishes to give her son what he wants but, in the same act, she wishes to make her sister jealous and to defy her mother. The tender components of the introject are directed toward her son, the angry, sexually defiant components are directed against her sister and mother—with threats to become a prostitute and disgrace the family. We can see that this is a complicated response, based on Anne's past experience, to a rather simple stimulus, the story about the hamburgers.

Even young babies are highly selective about the experiences they introject or take into themselves and later identify with and the ones they ignore or spit out, to paraphrase Freud. This has a great deal to do with the forming of the individuality of the child. In addition to the child's own choice of what it wishes to learn, is added the fact that, culturally, parents tend actively to teach the child and to draw the child's attention to certain types of learning. There is no doubt that part of the differentiation between boy and girl, which probably starts in the latter half of the first year of the baby's life, is a result of specific attitudes that the parents show toward the baby, as well as the fact that there is probably a highly specific biological difference in the interests and the types of experiences that little girls seek out from those which little boys seek out. The two of these together (one, the parents' teaching, and two, the child's actively seeking experiences) cause the child to develop along the patterns that both it and its parents have set for itself. All development follows along this path in the sense that everyone wishes to express individuality. Yet, in expressing individuality, there must be some adjustment to the needs of other people.

Partly because this is a period when the baby is toilet-trained and partly because it is an extension of the baby's eagerness to learn with which sex to identify itself, the child shows great curiosity about how people go to the bathroom. The difference between the sexes is usually discovered by watching other children or the parents excrete. At this time, the child may show coprophilic impulses which, in dreams, seem to be related to curiosity about the difference between the sexes. Again, to find out is to eat. To find out the techniques for excretion which the child will use all of his life is something that is discovered and then introjected. It is at this period that the child begins to want to break into the bathroom whenever the parents go. The differentiation between male and female first centers around whether one sits or stands to urinate and, probably, only later around whether one has a penis or not. It is in experiences such as these that the little girl finds out that she is like her mother rather than her father.

The child's first impulses toward the father are oral ones and, in a very real sense, psychologically, the child regards him as something pleasurable and different to eat than the mother. When the penis is discovered, usually sometime in the second year of life, the impulses toward it are again oral; it is looked on as a nipple (Freud), another source of oral gratification to which the child may respond as she did originally to the mother with the wish to excrete in order to please the father. At this early stage, the child has a strong desire to have her father see her on the toilet and wishes to win his love, as she had earlier wished to win her mother's love, by going to the bathroom for him. If the early relationship with the mother is good, this is easily transferred to the father.

Around this time, there develops in the little girl a competitive attitude toward the mother, with some wish for recognition of the fact that she is like the mother and competing with her. This, in larval form, is the *anlage* of the first heterosexual competition with the mother. It is not at all uncommon to have this competitive situation come up in the manifest content of dreams in adult women as a regression from the Oedipus complex. Anne's dream above is a variation of the same theme with the son, in the latent content of the dream, taking the place of the father and the wish for the father hidden under the latent dream wish of being a prostitute. While the metabolism described above certainly occurs in the little girl's phantasy about her father, the main source of oral gratification still remains the mother. In addition, of course, the real food she eats is given to her by the mother. So we get a triangular conflict developing on the level of eating and excreting.

We now come to one of the early triangular conflicts: the child identifies the food the mother gives her, along with all the other things that she has received or learned from the mother, as something that may be turned into gift excreta for the father. One form frequently taken by pre-Oedipal conflicts is that the child becomes afraid to eat in the father's presence because of the fear of having her gastro-colic reflex stimulated. She will be able to eat when alone or when with mother but cannot eat when father is around because of the wish and the fear of drawing his attention to any need to go to stool. I would regard this solution as the forerunner of a homosexual one. Whereas the little boy, at a similar stage, knows his excreta have come from mother's food and gives back to her what he got in an attempt to seduce her, the little girl phantasies, in giving to father, that she has robbed mother and has to face her hostility. Whatever the original phantasies of the little girl are in this regard, they are deeply reinforced by hostility on the part of the mother.

As the child grows older, her wish to compete with mother now takes the form—instead of eating and excreting for father—

of getting a baby from him by the oral route and producing a child through the rectum. This is the logical outgrowth of the previously purely oral and anal phantasies and is frequently precipitated by seeing the mother or other close relatives pregnant. By the time of the Oedipal phase, which usually occurs between the ages of four and six, the child, because of her own sexual feelings and her identification with mother, develops the wish to be penetrated vaginally by the father and to produce a baby in this way.

Patients who develop strong homosexual or masculine protest conflicts almost universally have an intolerance for triangular relationships. This intolerance is the result of traumatic relationships with both parents, the mother who is jealous of the child's relationship with the father and the father who is jealous of the child's relationship with the mother and other men. In my experience, women who have had a good relationship with one parent—even though the other parent may be very neurotic—will not develop overt homosexuality. In homosexuals, one sees that the relationship with the mother has to exclude the father. One the other hand, as Helen Deutsch and Freud and others have pointed out, these patients almost all have a very strong Oedipus complex with a marked father attachment in the unconscious or pre-conscious. In my experience, the relationship with the father has also to be a one-to-one relationship, with an intolerance for relating to other men or women. Homosexual women will show almost as much guilt toward father over their interest in mother as they did, in the original Oedipal situation, toward mother over the interest in father.

Because sexual impulses arise before the child is mature enough physically or has enough knowledge to handle them, sexual wishes are always reacted to with fear, ambivalence and inadequacy. When such feelings arise, the little girl normally wants to turn to the mother for help and reassurance; she also wants to learn the mother's techniques in order to identify with her. So, in a small girl, the early Oedipal strivings toward the father are reacted to with increased dependent longings for mother's help.

We now come to the problem of sexual dependence which I shall try to describe from the point of view of the little girl in her Oedipal period. She wishes to "marry" father but is aware that she is sexually undeveloped and ignorant. Moreover, she has a dread of the sexual act, not only because she is afraid of her father's big penis and what it could do to her but also because of her highly ambivalent fear of having a child and her fear of failure with father. So, at a time when she is by no means ready to give up her father and look for another object but, instead, wishes to kill her mother or at least throw her out and take her place with father, she needs that same mother's help very badly. Her sense of reality is not well enough developed for her to be aware of the fact that she cannot grow up overnight and her dependent phantasies toward the mother have an oral coloring which ties up this conflict with the conflicts of the preceding stages. Her interest and curiosity about the mother has shifted to the genitals and away from the breast, except as the breast is a symbol of sex appeal. On the oral cannibalistic level, she phantasies "if only I had my mother's genitals (often represented as pubic hair and breasts), I could take her place with father." To this orally castrative wish against the mother is attached anything she wants to learn from her— anything, that is, which in her mind is connected with sex or which, she thinks, might make her more adequate sexually; also, all gifts she has received from the mother which would contribute to this aim.

Probably every little girl has some castrative wishes toward her mother because of the Oedipal rivalry and the wish to be the only one father loves. These wishes are normally outgrown and/or repressed. Their place is taken by the more normal receptive wishes to be loved by and to learn from mother. This happens, that is, if the mother is able to be helpful and encouraging about her relationship with father. The unconscious hostile wishes will be reinforced by a jealous non-giving mother who rejects the child's Oedipal sexuality and does not encourage her sublimations with her father.

I shall now present, in diagrammatic form, the sexual dependence on the mother, its triangular nature and its normal outcome. Starting at the bottom, we see the little girl sexually stimulated by the father (Father 1). She develops anxiety be-

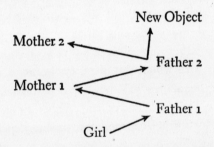

cause of her immaturity and because of her sexual phantasies, which are an outgrowth of her past experiences. Hence, she reacts with feelings of inadequacy and turns to the mother (Mother 1) for help. Both in relation to father and mother, her feelings are passive-receptive. On the oral level, she has impulses in the direction of her mother's genitals which may or may not be cannibalistic; in any case, they are important for learning purposes—in the sense that the child has to find out what the mother does and to identify with it, at least in part, before she can become feminine. For instance, on the anal level, if the child gets herself dirty, she needs to have the mother clean her up and make her attractive before she can turn back to the father for love. If the relationship with the mother is good and the mother has been able to help the child on a level which the child can accept, the latter has learned something and can now go back to her father (Father 2) with an active feminine attitude, displaying this new identification with mother which, naturally, has its competitive aspects. If father can praise her without being too seductive, and if she can also go back to mother (Mother 2 in the diagram) without too much guilt and fear, the child has made a real step toward feminine maturity. The relationship to both mother and father has shown her that her Oedipal phantasies are not gratified in reality; but, in their place, she can get both her father's and mother's love for feminine accomplishments and she can take pleasure in the knowledge that she is learning to grow up. As she becomes confident with father, she will seek out new masculine objects—the little boys with whom she plays, for instance, about whom her feminine phantasies will now revolve. Thus, even at an early age, the little girl makes trial flights from the nest to return home for further learning and further dependent forms of gratification. The diagram is presented as a zigzag, rather than a triangle, to indicate the shift in libido position from passive dependence to active independence in relationship to both parents and to new objects.

Two qualifying adjectives for the word dependence may be useful here: "progressive" and "regressive." While analysts in general attempt to avoid value judgments, it is important and clinically useful to define the different types of dependence—since, in analytic literature, the word dependence is usually used in a regressive sense. Therefore, I shall attempt to define progressive dependence first. Progressive dependence is an attempt to gain dependent satisfaction (help) in order to attain active mastery over a problem. For instance, if the little girl's original wish to eat mother's food in order to give father a bowel movement has been successfully outgrown, at a later date, the little girl will want to learn how to cook in order to give father food. She had to learn this from mother and is thus, temporarily, dependent on her. The dependence, however, serves a purpose; it helps her to become active and mature. That is what I call progressive dependence; it is seen in all situations where the child wishes to learn or to acquire objects which make her more mature. The little girl's wish to have a pretty dress which will make her more attractive to father is a progressive dependent wish. Regressive dependence is a flight away from maturity, from the wish to learn and the wish to master actively the techniques of growing up. It is instead, a wish to go back to previous modes of adaptation which caused the child some satisfaction in the past. Such regressive dependence is one of the hallmarks of homosexual activity which renounces mature heterosexuality in favor of infantile oral or aggressive phantasies and acting out.

When the child grows in confidence that she can win father's love, she makes attempts at positive relationships with other males. This leads her to abandon the Oedipal attachment. However, if the father is jealous and feels threatened by the sexual manifestations of his child, especially her interest in males, the child also develops a severe conflict in the father transference just as she has with the mother. Then, when she wishes to relate to boys, she may feel that she has robbed her father of his position and she may become as frightened of his jealousy as she was of the mother's jealousy in the Oedipal situation. This I consider one of the major post-Oedipal con-

flicts with the father and a very important source of homosexuality; turning from father to women carries with it less
guilt about him, and hence less fear, than leaving him for a
new male object. As one female homosexual, whose father
had repeatedly admonished her not to let boys touch her, said,
"He never told me not to be homosexual."

So far, I have attempted to draw a picture of what I regard
as normal development. This picture is drawn from the theories
of Freud and other anaylsts, with some additions from my own
clinical experience. Now I shall attempt to differentiate carefully between normal and homosexual attitudes. Since the
meaning of homosexuality is the perversion or turning away
of instincts from their normal heterosexual channels into other
channels, I shall attempt to divide the relationships of the
little girl with her mother into three categories: the normal,
the disturbed and the perverse. The normal has already been
described. Disturbed relationships occur where there is conflict over sex but no compromise has been made about the
conscious heterosexual wishes. Freud's formulation of perversion
was any sexual act in which orgasm is not completed in the
heterosexual act. Many types of phantasy which recapitulate
the historical past of the individual are normal, according to
Freud. The oral receptive and anal defiant impulses that I have
described above are all normal and part of the development of
every child. Such impulses become homosexual only when
they are short-circuited. The normal response to learning about
sex from mother is heterosexual phantasies or their sublimation
in active behavior.

Homosexuality arises out of anxiety. Metaphorically, one learns
by introjecting, which, in the unconscious, means swallowing.
Yet actual homosexual oral acting out usually precludes learning
because of the guilt and anxiety felt toward the partner. One

might say that the acting out of such homosexual impulses is a perversion of the normal wish to learn. On the other hand, the acting out of aggressive homosexual play is again a perversion of the normal wish to compete with a person of one's own sex. An overt homosexual girl, consciously in love with a maternal partner, was happy "giving" her orgasms to her girl friend until she discovered that she had the unconscious phantasy that, if she had an orgasm with a man, it would kill her friend.

Masculine protest or penis envy is not always homosexual in character, although it may be. In the little girl, the wish to have a penis may be purely defensive in character, an attempt to deny heterosexuality without concomitant homosexual feelings. In a family where there is a favorite brother, the little girl may want to be a boy in order to be more loved or better fed by her mother. When penis envy in relation to a brother was interpreted to a patient of mine, she burst into tears and cried, "Mother never bought me strawberries out of season as she did for my brother." This was especially painful to the patient, since she had, in previous dreams, identified strawberries with her mother's menses and her own pre-pubertal longing to menstruate. Dr. Jacob Kasanin reported the following delusion of a psychotic woman: "I know I am a snake because they are feeding me corn meal and milk." It is obvious that this patient feared she would be starved if she were not masculine. Both Rado and Melanie Klein have shown how the wish for a penis may be due to aggressiveness against the mother; in other words, the penis is regarded as a weapon that can be used in battle against a dangerous mother. Later on, I shall give an illustration from the dream of a patient who wanted to be masculine because she felt that the only way to learn her mother's sexual secrets was to have a penis; in the unconscious, the penis is often a scoptophilic organ because of its function of penetration.

The following is a clinical instance of how homosexual feelings can arise. We take the small child at the level of her Oedipal period and at the height of her father attachment. She is sexually stimulated by father and turns to mother for help. Mother punishes her, physically or mentally, for disclosing her Oedipal wishes. It doesn't take many such experiences to make the child believe that she is caught in a hopeless situation and that her life is in danger from the mother. This is not only because of the latter's actual behavior, the phantasy is partly a reaction to the child's own Oedipally derived death wishes against the mother, reinforced as these are by the fear and anger the mother's attitude arouses. The next time she is sexually stirred by the father, she will tend to conceal the real state of affairs by convincing both mother and herself that she really prefers the mother and is, in fact, in love with her. We thus arrive at the homosexual declaration as a defense against the Oedipal wish.

Cora, a homosexual girl, after about five hours—it was her second analysis—came in and announced that she was in love with me and that she had been in love with her previous analyst, also a woman. She spent about half the hour cheerfully proving her point. The only issue was whether I would object to her homosexuality but, being reassured, she was able to continue. Finally she came out with the following dream:

"I was in a store. The woman who owned it was fat and had an apron on. I pushed her aside and grabbed two chocolate bars."

After admitting that the dream didn't sound very homosexual, she was asked to associate to the two chocolate bars. She blurted out, "I don't know why I think of this but I heard your husband give a lecture a year ago and I think he is very good-looking. I wish you had two of them." Whereupon she burst out crying. By deceiving herself about her main conflict, she could be relatively unemotional and self-possessed until her unconscious Oedipal wishes broke through in her associations. In the same way, a small child can defend herself against fear by believing the sexual feeling she has is directed toward mother.

However, this attempt at a homosexual solution is a mere stopgap. The child has, in phantasy, saved her life but she has not satisfied her heterosexual dependent longings. The Oedipal feelings arise again and, along with them, the accompanying helpless dependent ones for the mother. The child, frustrated in her dependent wishes, notices that father or brother figures can get more from mother than she. She concludes that, if she were male and loved mother, she could get more from mother. Thereafter, instead of merely denying her sexual feelings toward father, she tries to convince mother that her feelings toward mother are masculine. Here we see that masculinity is a meal ticket as far as mother is concerned and a magical and unconsciously dishonest means of gaining dependent satisfaction.

Clara, to whom the interpretation had been given, the day before, that she wished to have a penis in order to ferret out her mother's sexual secrets, dreamed:

"I was in a house where I saw a fox. The woman of the house thought it was a ferret. I didn't tell her of her error."

Her associations to the fox brought out a story she had read about a woman who kept a fox as a pet. This fox was very friendly to a man the woman hated. As she read the story, Clara wondered how long the woman would keep the fox as a pet if she were aware of its attachment to the man. In the dream, she is saying, "You may think I am a ferret [masculine] if it suits you. Actually, I am being foxy and deceiving you as to my real feelings for father. If you knew, you would throw me out and not take care of me any more."

I shall quote from a dream communicated to me by Dr. Harry Lee some years ago, where the masculine identification is successful in gaining sexual dependent satisfaction. The patient was a woman who was insecure with mother figures and had a strong masculine protest.

> "I saw a white peacock going into a house. [The father in the primal scene]. Although he was beautiful before he went into the house, he was even more beautiful when he came out. So I decided to go in also. He looked at me angrily but I went in. When I got inside, I found two beautiful blue dresses, one a bright blue like the sky at midday and the other a midnight-blue. I took both out with me."

Later in the dream, she gives the midnight-blue dress to an older woman as restitution but keeps the more seductive midday-blue dress for herself. The problem in the case of this woman was her belief that, in order to get anything from mother, she had to masquerade as a man even up to and including the sexual act. However, the feminine wishes break through and she gets something from mother which enhances her femininity during the masculine indentification with father in the primal scene and, later in the dream, makes restitution to a mother figure as well. It is easy to see the difference in this "masculine" dream of a young woman and the really masculine dream of a man.

Another dream, later in the analysis, again shows the masculine strivings in the service of her feminine longings on the way to resolution:

> "I dove into a pool looking for something. At the bottom of the pool were baubles which I recognized as cheap but, never-

theless, I reached for them but they always escaped my hands. I rose to the top of the pool and saw you [the analyst] there waiting for me. I reached out my hand to you and, as I did so, I realized something was in my hand which had been there all the time but I had been unaware of it. It was a small gold object, either a statuette of a girl or a baby—I don't know which."

Here the patient is recognizing that the masculine dependent relationship with mother is no longer necessary, that she already has what it takes to interest a father figure. And, last but not least, she is not afraid to believe it is better than what mother has. She is seeing the creative aspect of competitiveness (the baby).

One more example from Anne's analysis shows how homosexuality can mask a conflictful anxiety-ridden dependence on a female analyst. Anne had come to me after a stormy unsuccessful analysis of at least five years' duration with a male analyst. During the course of this analysis, she had started to act out sexually and had had many promiscuous relationships. Her early communications were masked in chatter, blaming her ex-analyst for her plight and displaying much conscious hostility of a castrative nature to him. She justified this attitude by her belief in the ineffectuality of her previous analysis; obviously, however, she was hoping that this castrative hostile behavior to a father figure would win my love. After several hours, she had the following dream:

"It was a sorority initiation. The girls were naked and on all fours in a circle. They were all licking the genitals of the girls in front of them. The girl behind me was licking mine but I would not lick the genitals of the girl in front because there was chewing gum on them."

Anne started her associations in her usual superficial manner. She supposed she was in love with me. Her male analyst had told her she was homosexual and would throw any man down for a woman any day. This went on for some time until she was interrupted and asked to associate to the cunnilingus. At this point, a dramatic change took place in the patient's behavior. She began to cry violently and finally was able to give the following associations: She was the third child of four girls born in the depths of a depression. Her family had wanted a boy, not a girl. Her mother had been so overburdened with work and so rejecting of the child, in addition, that she would put the baby in a basket and hoist it to the ceiling of the kitchen and neglect her. It was a hot summer and the baby's face became all flyspecked. One day, her aunt came in and saw the baby's plight and washed her up. This story she had heard in her childhood. She remembered her mother giving her very little physical care and attacking everything she did to make herself attractive; so, as a small child, she felt dirty and unattractive. In addition, both parents were very hostile to her sexuality, especially her mother. When she was five or six, she remembered watching a mother cat washing its kittens by licking them. At the time, she thought how pretty and clean the little kittens looked and how the mother must really love them since she even licked their genitals. Shortly after this, she induced her younger sister to lick her genitals but she refused to lick the sister's, just as she had in the dream.

The interpretation given Anne was that she felt dirty and degraded by what had happened to her; she wished to be cleaned up, as she had wished her mother to clean her up as a child, so she could feel attractive again, but she despaired of help unless she became a homosexual and gave up all men. In effect, this was what she had been doing in the early hours of the analysis with her castrative onslaughts on her ex-analyst and other men. The other motive for homosexuality emerges in the last part of the dream, where Anne refuses to lick the genitals of the woman in front of her. The associations to this part of the dream were given in a later hour. The most pertinent one was to the gum, which called up the memory of the fact that her mother forbade the children to chew gum though Anne was aware that the mother herself chewed it behind their backs. This was a screen memory for the primal scene. Anne told of her shocked discovery—which aroused in her intense rage and jealousy—that the mother was having sexual relationships with the father while she told the children that sex was the worst thing in the world. The obvious fact—that Anne expected help from me with her heterosexuality but couldn't face her mother's sexuality because of her rage at and fear of the primal scene—threw light on why she expressed so much guilt over the one-sided homosexual relationship she had with her sister. She was trying to play a homosexual game with me and her sister in which we both were homosexualized so that Anne wouldn't have to face the primal scene, while unconsciously she intended to desert mother and sister once her dependent longings were gratified and go away with father.

This brings up another problem: why the whole issue had to be homosexualized. Here there are several economic levels.

1. She had to keep from a mother figure the wish to be made attractive in father's eyes because she feared that, otherwise, her needs wouldn't be satisfied. Hence her homosexual regression.

2. Insofar as she conceived attractiveness as something given by mother, the early toilet training, which was strict, demanded that all sexuality so gained had to be returned to mother in the form of an orgasm, just as all food she got from her mother had to be returned in the form of feces. This she did in the dream in letting the girl behind her lick her genitals.

3. Last but not least, her conscience demanded that she

do as much for mother as she wished mother to do for her—the expectation in the dream that she was to lick the genitals of the girl in front of her—but, so her phantasy went, if she did that for mother, then mother would be more attractive to father and this she couldn't stand. In its place and as a defense against the primal scene, she phantasies but does not act out in the dream the wish to take mother's orgasm away from her orally and thus castrate her before she can get to father.

Most of these homosexual dependent relationships are disappointing to the patient. Even though they may have, in fact, acquired much of their partner's secret information by trickery, they feel too guilty and too fearful of her rage to try out their new-found skills on father. Especially was this true of the patient in the fox dream. In her adolescence—at the suggestion of an older, very attractive female relative—she had had her hair cut like a boy's. With this boyish haircut, she succeeded in gaining the friendship of one of the most attractive girls in college but she never allowed herself to compete with this girl and remained feeling unhappy and unattractive to men. The relationship was not overtly homosexual but an assumption of submissive masculinity in the hope of getting help.

The problem now arises why there should be the necessity of orgasm or sexual contact with a person of one's own sex. The dependent homosexual act consists of a phantasied oral castration of the partner in the service of dependent and hostile longings; the resulting orgasm represents a giving back to mother—or a self-castration—of all that one has received, as one gave back the stool to mother as a child. The phantasy is that there is nothing left over for a man and the patient does not allow herself to give to a man or even to be aware of the wish to give.

Where the conscious phantasy is an active masculine wish

to penetrate a woman in order to give her satisfaction, the unconscious orally colored phantasies of phallic oral exploitation of mother demand the restitution of what one has received and the orgasm is again a self-castrative, restitutive act.

So far, we have discussed the problem of dependence where the dependent longings are denied by a hostile mother. However, there is also the child's unwillingness to face the facts of sex, based on her jealousy of the mother's relationship with the father. In this connection, I shall quote a pair of Anne's dreams from the same night, some months after the cunnilingus dream. At the time of these dreams, she was still struggling with the problem of trying to find out "what it is to be a woman."

Dream 1. "I was looking at a beautiful brown and yellow flower. The harder I looked, the less I could see. It kept blurring."

Dream 2. "A man was getting something for me out of a toilet with a stick which had a suction cup on the end of it."

Anne's associations led to memories of the prettiest hat her mother had ever had, a brown velvet with yellow flowers. Following these associations, the anal identification of these colors came up as well as her rage at the sexuality of her mother who had had relations with her father "behind the backs of her children." She felt her mother was dirty.

The following interpretation was given: "You can't find out what it is to be a woman because you don't want to face your mother's sexuality. When you are thwarted in your curiosity, you turn to father for help." (Dream 2.)

Anne laughed and confirmed the interpretation by saying that, the night before, she had gone out with a man who had spent the evening boasting about his exploits with other women and that she was aware of being furiously angry at him.

In these dreams, her receptiveness is thwarted by her own unwillingness to know. Her typical solution of the problem was a homosexual regression in which she and a mother or sister figure loved only each other and there was no possibility of the primal scene.

Such patients develop a pseudo-dependency in which they utilize their strong conscious need for help from mother to keep her away from father. Their dependent needs are never satisfied because they can't accept the very thing they want to learn, namely, that heterosexuality is permissable for them; if it is permissible for them, it is also permissible for mother, and that they cannot tolerate.

The Cunnic Father*

I have coined this term as a parallel term to phallic mother, and will now define it. Many girls do not take "no" for an answer from mother nor do they homosexualize their relationship with her other than briefly. They leave mother disappointed in their dependent longings and, instead of being able to turn to father in an active, giving feminine way, they turn to him still with sexual feeling but with strong oral dependent wishes as well. The content of the latter is: "Give me what mother never gave me," and, "Rob her to get it. I can't, not being a man." Their phantasy of the sexual act is that, in it, they will acquire something of mother's from father which he has acquired from mother by means of the sexual act. As the primal scene phantasies unfold and as the patient's sadism toward her mother becomes freer, we see father's penis identified with a devouring rat or a knife which he uses to cut mother up.

* The father who is equipped with male and female sex organs in phantasy.

I shall give the dreams of three different women to show the role of the cunnic father; they range from a purely oral receptive dream to a dream with murderous orally aggressive associations.

Jane had only recently given up her homosexual transference and was becoming increasingly interested in men when she had the following dream:

> "Other children and I [as a child] were standing in line waiting to get into a banquet hall. A big man picked me up and put me at the head of the line and led me in. People had already eaten but, on a table, I saw an olive with a bite taken out of it and an eggplant."

The man who picked her up was associated to a married doctor, an acquaintance of ours to whom Jane was attracted. He was also associated to a Santa Claus who had kissed her as a child and to a doctor who had held her on his lap and kissed her, likewise during her childhood. So the Oedipal sexual references in the dream are clear. The eggplant reminded her of her early curiosity about pregnancy. The olive with a bite taken out of it reminded her of an illustration she had seen of a gonorrheal cervix and her old curiosity about prostitutes. Here she is expecting from the sexual act some satisfaction of her curiosity about mother. The reference to "people had already eaten" was a primal scene phantasy.

May, a woman with strong conscious homosexual phantasies, was just reaching the point where she could see her sexual competition with the mother for the father. One day, at the end of the hour, she confided that she had always thought of her orgasm as a large golden ball breaking into thousands of brightly colored pieces.

The next day she was disturbed and panicky because she had had an almost irresistible impulse to break into the office of Doctor X, a colleague of mine, and demand sexual relations.

That night she had the following dream which she referred
to as a "sexual dream":

"The clerk at the A&P gave me an orange which was my
mother's orgasm."

Her first association to the dream was, "It didn't look like
much compared to mine," referring to her phantasy of her own
orgasm the day before. The first part of the hour was filled with
anxious associations relating to the overwhelming nature of her
sexual impulses toward Dr. X, who bore a marked physical
resemblance to her father. She was brought back several times
to the orange but to no avail. Finally I asked, "What does
getting something of mother's from Dr. X mean to you?" The
following came out with a rush, "If Dr. X were my father,
I should like to tell him my philosophy of life and have him
tell me it was better than my mother's. If it wasn't, I would
sit at his feet and learn from him until my philosophy of life
became better than hers." Two things are interesting here:
(1) that the patient associated her philosophy of life, that is,
something learned, with her sexuality (she had a tremendous
admiration for her mother's philosophy of life which, according
to her, was the one beautiful thing her mother, a very jealous
and hostile person, had); and (2), that, insofar as her father
was willing to communicate any of her mother's ideals to her,
she felt that her ungiving mother was robbed. She equated this
robbery with the sexual act with father.

The third dream was that of a young girl who had always
been intensely heterosexual and unusually attractive to men, a
fact about which she felt extremely guilty. Sometime during her
second year of analysis, she had the following dream:

"My slip was stained with blood."

The association to the dream was an obscene French story
which she had once read. The story was about an Egyptian

temple—a house of prostitution. A young and very beautiful girl becomes an inmate. An older man, who was the lover of the chief priestess, wished to have the first night with this young girl. The girl demands as her price that he give her the pearl necklace of the chief priestess and a piece of jewelry belonging to the statue of Isis. The man agrees. He steals the jewelry from the statue, after which he goes to the priestess who is his mistress, makes love to her to disarm her, stabs and kills her, comes to the young girl with the booty and then has intercourse with her. The bloodstain on the patient's slip in the dream is identified with that of the young girl's first intercourse and is evidence to the patient that she, too, had wished to be the partner in an incestuous crime against her mother. During this hour, she had severe uterine cramps although she was not menstruating.

Although these Oedipal phantasies are in the service of sexual dependency and oral aggressivity directed toward the mother, the father is not conceived of as a mother image, but as a powerful figure who is sadistic and castrative toward the mother out of love for his daughter. Men who play such a striking role in their daughter's lives are those who are, in reality, hostile to their wives and favor the daughter over the mother; they are conceived of as in no way maternal. A daughter who has so cathected a father regards him as a heroic figure. The Oedipal victory over the mother involves, in the child's mind, the castration and/or death of the mother at the father's hands. The fathers of such patients, in my experience, have been more than normally jealous of both their wives and daughters. Hence the "Oedipal victory" is frequently handed to the daughter when the mother has made the father jealous. The result is that the daughter is forced into a father fixation, first in competition with the "unfaithful" mother and, secondly, out of fear that, if she herself is "unfaithful," he will wreak upon her the same retaliation she has phantasied he wreaked upon her mother. So, in addition to whatever receptive expectations she has from her father, she is afraid to move away from him because of castration fear should she make him jealous. This castration fear exists on two levels. The one is fear of direct physical damage from him and the second is fear of his intercourse with another woman in which the patient fears castration, as she phantasies she and her father could castrate mother in an incestuous relationship.

As a result, when the girl experiences temptation from a new object, the way back to father is blocked by intense fear. She dreads the primal scene and tries to prevent it, this time by a homosexual relationship with a woman who stands in some way or other for the hated mother. The homosexual act, as a defense against being unfaithful to father, accomplishes several ends.

1. The partner (mother, in the unconscious) phantasy protects her from father.

2. By orally castrating the partner (mother) in phantasy, she defends herself against the primal scene.

3. By convincing herself (and the father in phantasy or reality) that she is homosexual, she avoids fear of the retaliation that she expects from him were she to desert him for another man.

Summary

This has been an attempt to show how homosexuality and masculine identification may serve as a protection against anxiety and to trace the morbid process back to its earliest developmental sources.

The mechanism by which homosexuality accomplishes so

much is inherent in its tendency to reduce triangular relationships to two-way relationships. In giving up the father attachment, the girl goes back to a two-way relationship with a
mother-sister figure in which, in phantasy, all real love comes
from the partner and all real giving goes to the partner. Of
course, in reality, a homosexual or any other type of human
relationship cannot exist without a longing to break away to
new contacts. Therefore the homosexual relationship is a conflictful one.

The Oedipal relationship, if well developed, as it usually is in
homosexuals, is also an attempt at a two-way relationship. It
consists symbolically, in getting rid of mother, thus permitting
a phantasied exclusive relationship with father, in which all
dependence comes from him and all giving goes to him. So a
relationship which is a caricature of sexual fidelity exists until
it is broken, usually by the father's showing an interest in someone else. In spite of her disappointment in him, the patient is
unable to go on to another man because of fear of retaliation
on the father's part, and so, for a second time, she is forced
back into homosexuality.

The Relation Between Submission and Aggression in Male Homosexuality

MILTON L. MILLER

Psychoanalytic experience with homosexual male patients reveals this characteristic in them: a split response to a stimulus that provokes aggression. Rivalrous aggression is expressed concomitantly with a submissive urge which is linked to the need for continued protection. And, vice versa, their expression of feminine submissiveness is apt to be accompanied by overt or disguised aggression, sometimes in the form of a seemingly remote symptom or personality defect. During the process of therapy, both sides of an especially strong ambivalence are likely to be stimulated in the transference; that is one of the reasons so many homosexual patients are difficult to help.

During therapy, the erotized, feminine approach of the homosexual male is gradually unmasked as a threatening Medusa-like weapon; the unmasking occurs when competition with the father or hostility to stronger men or toward siblings is mobilized. A number of latent attitudes* are involved which

* There is an admixture of various motivations in most of the homosexual cases under treatment: flight from incest, identification with the

160

one may find, in a wide range of patients, frequently disguised and dissociated, so that the connection between the aggressive and submissive or erotized components is not easily discernible unless one is aware of how the homosexual conflict is based on paradoxical aspects of the sexual function. Because masculine identification with a virile father is inhibited or undeveloped, both hostility and erotization seek an expression based on identification with the female.

The dynamic elements of feminine identification were clearly illustrated in a male hospital employee in his late twenties who entered analysis because of depression. He was markedly withdrawn from human relationships, except for the homosexual affairs of which he was ashamed.

The patient had lost his mother when he was six years of age. Before that, his childhood had been fairly pleasant although he remembers strict punishment by his mother, being hit over the head with a belt, for instance. For a long time before his mother's death, his father had been away on business and the boy had his mother all to himself. Then his father returned and pre-empted the boy's place as center of the household; shortly after that, a baby brother was born. Several weeks after the baby's birth, the patient's mother died of pneumonia. The father became depressed and very withdrawn for a time. Later, he remarried. The patient grew up with a sullen disposition, and a dislike for his father, brother and stepmother. He described himself as like a sterilized cat the family had, which had nothing to do with anybody. He loved young boys in the way he seemed to wish his mother had continued to love him, according to the frequently seen pattern. Whenever he felt

mother, narcissistic love of the beloved boy with whom the patient also identifies, castration fear, submission to the father out of regard or fear, and a history of sexual seduction or intimidation, masochistic and sadistic elements, anal fixation, etc.

threatened by overwhelming feelings of despondency, frustration and depression, he would have a homosexual affair. The patient had repressed his rage at his mother's desertion of him in death. His oral relationship to her had never been resolved, and, as we shall see, the tearing, biting, oral-sadistic elements were clear in his dreams. His aggression against his father had not been integrated into his personality, permitting inadequate identification with the father's masculinity.

His aggression toward his everyday environment was overcompensated; he functioned successfully as a hospital employee, very often neglecting his own welfare in order to see that hospital patients were treated with kindness and consideration. He often got into arguments with other hospital employees, medical men, etc., because of his extreme consideration for the patients. During his analysis, he became aware of rivalrous hostility toward his father and younger brother. After reading about an abortionist in the newspaper, he spontaneously commented that he, himself, had the personality make-up to be an abortionist. When his sister had a baby, he was upset and had dreams and phantasies of its destruction.

It was at this time, when the hostile rivalry toward his brother was more conscious, that he thought about making his first date with a girl. In a half-hearted manner, he invited her to a concert. That night he dreamed:

> He was cleaning a room with a vacuum cleaner. It picked up the cat and took it all the way in except for the head, which was showing. The cat's head had over its nose and face a crystal cup (later, he called it a plastic cup). With the help of some others, like a group of doctors, he got the cat out and, although its body was flattened, it blew up again to normal shape.

His associations were: the cat is their cat at home, Mephisto (the castrated cat). Deplorable that it could not go out and have a sexual outlet. The same with their dog. The family treated these animals cruelly. The cat was aloof and had nothing to do with anybody. The vacuum cleaner reminded him of a conversation with a homosexual acquaintance with whom he had started an affair. They were talking about a man whose penis got stuck in a vacuum cleaner.

Then he thought of a male television star who had, the preceding evening, received a present of an ostrich egg, with a chain and lock on it, covered with plastic on a stand.

This led to thoughts of the girl whom he had "sort of invited" to attend a concert with him; but she was too busy, he said. He felt uneasy with her.

The thing on the cat's face, in the dream, reminded him of the apparatus for a little girl who had been operated on.

From the above condensation of his associations, we can see how the patient's attitude toward the prospect of a mild heterosexual gesture, just inviting a girl to a concert, was to try to control the entire frightening subject of sexuality, in all its aspects, by identifying with the birth-giving female. Recalling the image of a toothless Hallowe'en witch on her broomstick, he created a vacuum cleaner image that swept out rooms in a frightening way. He holds the phallic stick, in the dream, and he also controls the powerful bag that sucks everything into it. With it, he is doing something helpful, cleaning away dirt— also, of course, a denial of anal aggression. But the cat is stuck in it; it is a castrated male cat, Mephisto, toward whom he offers protection, help and sympathy. The cat, flattened out by this sadistic event—with its implications of erotization, primal scene and birth—is at the end brought back to normal.

Incidentally, the reference to change in size, in the dream, was typical of his preoccupation with his brother's stature and strength compared with his own. If his brother succeeded in going out with girls, the patient would console himself by thinking he was taller, heavier and more proficient in the gymnasium than his brother. Much of his spare time was devoted to physical exercise.

The main emphasis of the dream was on a recapitulation of the birth of the brother. The cat was dragged into the bag and he got it out; but he identified with the painful process. His brother's birth, which he unconsciously thought had killed his mother and traumatized himself, is reactivated in the dream. The feeling of being castrated like the cat, as a result of injury by the female organ, is an expression of the talion principle and is related to the repressed aggression he originally felt toward mother and brother, when the brother was born. (His homosexual identification with the woman reduced his fear of the female genitals and also his fear of punishment, for rivalry, by the father.)

This vacuum cleaner dream was a synopsis of the patient's personality problem and contained elements typical of most of his dreams. The dream represented a crystallization of his main conflicts. Most of his dreams demonstrated the same dynamic picture, stressing various specific angles or defenses, but implying the same total dynamic picture with great constancy, except that one could trace the diminishing inacessibility of the conflict, as well as the diminished withdrawal of the patient from human contacts, throughout the first year's dreams.

(For example: Very much earlier in the analysis, he saw a woman patient leaving the analyst's office; in response to this, he dreamed that he was going to Mexico with the governor's son to go into business making caviar there. He associated to this: thoughts of pregnancy and his dislike for slimy eggs. The sight of a woman connected with the analyst had immediately suggested unconscious thoughts of a possible pregnancy and his flight from the scene, his homosexual defense, and the restitution in the birth process which, at the same time, disgusted him. . . . A few months after the caviar dream, but before the vacuum cleaner dream, he had intermediary dreams which showed increasing recognition that he had heterosexual urges, and great fear of them.)

It was in the vacuum cleaner dream that he most clearly recapitulated the main trauma: the death of his mother and the birth of his baby brother. He tried to make up for the wish for his mother's love by being the mother himself in his attitude toward hospital patients and toward his homosexual objects. In his relations with men, he expressed an erotized form of his repressed aggression against his brother. His aggression toward his mother was actually so great that he had once named a cadaver, in medical school, with his mother's first name, without at the time noting the connection.

The vacuum cleaner dream demonstrated how a fairly simple problem like inviting a girl to a concert helped to provoke a dream which revolved around great fear of getting the woman pregnant, and of terrible punishment for this act. In the dream, the reference to birth, abortion and delivery, is quite apparent, as well as the retreat to the anal and oral levels, away from the genital level. He identifies himself with the woman and suffers as a result of the pregnancy. But he constantly tried to master this problem. So long as he associated only with men, he felt relatively safe; he was not faced with the fear of castration, which he felt as a retaliation for these repressed urges; with men, moreover, he was able to erotize some of his aggressions.

The patient's deep-rooted homosexuality was classical in its characteristics, that is, the oral, biting, tearing aggression toward the father, the identification with the female genital in hostility to the father, and the anal element: the urge to enjoy sex relations as the mother did, in a passive-receptive manner. His Oedipus complex—his hostile, competitive drives toward the father, displaced mainly to the brother—gave rise to sadistic urges which broke through mainly in his dreams and led to anxiety, guilt and masochism. He avoided competition, acted submissively, identified with his mother, and concentrated on what might be called the intermediary goals of his negative Oedipal situation: loving the younger boys, making restitution by kindness to patients. We should also note his voyeuristic and exhibitionistic defenses. In some dreams, he started with looking, only later becoming involved; he *sees* himself participating in these overcompensated birth scenes; he is, for instance, one of the group of men, like doctors, in the vacuum cleaner dream, looking at the cat and trying to help it until it resumes normal shape.

When he was able to maintain friendly relations with those whom he unconsciously considered his rivals, people like his younger brother or certain patients, he felt secure but, when the anal aggression and the oral aggression against these weaker people could not be held in check, he feared his mother's revenge. In the vacuum cleaner dream, the dirt and the suction that swallowed up the cat, with whom he also identified, represent powerful female aggression. His conflicts were so all-encompassing that he tended to withdraw from human relationships and to contain within himself the entire identification, constantly re-enacting the trauma. He tended to retreat to womb symbolism, soiling the woman, getting rid of the baby, identifying with the whole process, and making restitution. He also shows in the dream that the mother has a phallus, the vacuum cleaner he wields.

Such a dream demonstrates the simultaneous expression of

submission and aggression. The close relation between the submission and aggression in these patients is really based on a feeling of inadequacy and a need for protection. The need for protection is associated with the fear of the retaliation they anticipate because of their intense aggression.

This patient resembled other homosexual patients in that his relationship with his mother was very unsatisfactory. Here it was traumatically terminated. In some cases, the mothers were highly seductive and, at the same time, rejecting.

The bisexuality of homosexuals has been stressed by Freud.[1] If one is interested in mythological analogies, a rereading of the Perseus myth—particularly his use of the masculine symbol, the sword, against the sea monster, as well as his use of the feminine Medusa head against males—is of interest. It seems that, in homosexual men, the heterosexual relationship and pregnancy are so frightening that the strongest weapon is a bisexual one— or else whichever sexual weapon seems opportunistically most able to overwhelm the opponent.

The vacuum cleaner with the cat stuck in it—like the Medusa's head with the small snakes—was a symbol, to the patient quoted above, of the phallic female in conflict over giving birth to the frightening sibling (or siblings) and the phallic threat, along with denial of castration fear. Ferenczi[4] has pointed out the phallic symbolism of the Medusa but, in this image, the numerous small snakes also suggest the retaliatory venomous heads of hated siblings.

A second case tended to act out the ambivalent conflicts symbolized in the first patient's dream. This was an older man, an actor, who had gotten along fairly well until his middle years—leading a heterosexual existence and raising two children successfully—but with scattered homosexual episodes as well as homosexual phantasies and dreams. His neurosis had a chameleon-like quality, seeming to take on the coloration of the milieu and the times, so that he appeared to be the product of a maladjusted era, with heavy drinking and occasional sexual episodes with women or with men. His own father had been an alcoholic who had threatened his mother physically with a knife; he had finally left the family when the patient was about eight. The mother was extremely seductive and had been in collusion with the boy—an only child—in a castrative attitude toward the father.

This patient had eventually married a woman very much like his mother and had many stormy scenes with her. Their quarrels always seemed to be her fault. He had a talent for seducing people and making them do what he wanted them to do, which was the reason for his professional success, up to a certain point.

It became clear, in the analysis, that the appearance of adjustment to his surroundings masked a talent for projecting his conflicts on to others and manipulating the lives of others while his own life remained hollow and anxiety-ridden. In the transference, he had been adroit at flattery and at the same time made various attempts to look for weaknesses to which he might appeal, motivated by a desire to cripple the analyst's abilities. This desire to cripple the analyst, not only spiritually but physically, was related to memories of his father's appendectomy and difficult convalescence, when the patient was five. He had believed at the time that he had caused the illness by death wishes. During the analysis, whenever he became angry, he would dream of the analyst having a similar operation which the patient performed in one dream, for example, with scissors. When the full force of his aggression against both his father and the analyst came out, and when his guilt over his feelings toward his mother and his wife were mobilized, he was most inhibited in his work and dreamed of a broken arm, a broken turkey wing, a damaged airplane, etc., and finally could not work, felt futile, inadequate and childish. He felt the lack of a strong father with whom to identify. He identified with the alcoholism of his father and the insincere wiles, feminine exhibitionism and self-destructiveness of his mother. As his ambivalent feelings toward both parents became conscious, he had a good deal of conscious anxiety. Although he had come to analysis at first with the intention of proving that the analyst could not help him—and his unconscious motive was to act out by maintaining a seductively pleasant, homosexually tinged relation to the analyst—as his transference was mobilized, his hostility to the analyst became stronger and more conscious. He separated from his wife and children, declared to the analyst that he was really a homosexual—and had overt phantasies of seducing the analyst. Then, as a self-declared homosexual making every effort to exhibit failure as father and husband, he was able to bring out real masculine competition and aggression against the analyst. He then felt more free to do creative work.

In such patients as this one, the inability to deal with competitive masculine aggression is based on an inadequate relationship to the mother and, also, on an inability to identify successfully with the father in superego formation and in the varied aspects of the masculine role. Protection is craved at the very point when aggression is mobilized.

In some latently homosexual male patients who are not primarily in analysis for treatment of conscious homosexuality, a feminine attitude is suddenly exhibited and flaunted in the transference. Or it may be defended against quite superficially; but still the thinly disguised dependent, receptive, passive or feminine attitude is, at least for a time, the presenting layer, so that the patient avoids dealing with problems of masculine identification.

A third patient, who combined submissiveness to mother

figures to a perverse extent with homosexual impulses which were constantly held in check, was married and had three children, in spite of his aversion to heterosexuality. He led an outwardly respectable, conventional existence although he was anxious, withdrawn, and uneasy with his family. He was in a business owned by his older brothers. He had occasional impulses to kiss male business associates and perverse impulses, particularly masochistic urges, in regard to women. The latter he had, on rare occasions, secretly acted out. He was one of the category of men patients who desire to have a woman sit on their faces. The basis of the perversion in this case was inhibited sexual curiosity and hostility originally directed toward parental sexual activity, with a strong desire to keep parental coitus sterile—to avoid conception. The sexual relationship of his parents was imitated, according to infantile concepts, and controlled symbolically in his perversion. He was the youngest in a large family. During his analysis, his attitudes about money colored his dreams and associations; it became clear that, when he had impulses to extort money from business associates, or from his father or uncles or the analyst, his homosexuality and his perverse impulses were stimulated.

He, too, had been separated from his father when very young but the father and uncles had continued as a source of financial aid. The mother's personality had contributed toward his anal-erotic orientation and accidental early events had reinforced his tendency toward perversion—which, however, he usually managed to keep in check.

In the latter part of his analysis, the patient felt increased sexual interest in his wife; this occurred after he had gained some insight into his hostility toward his brothers, his uncles and his father. Currently, in the transference, he was dealing with wishes that the analyst take no new patients and fail in practice.

At this time, he dreamed that he saw a black spider about the size of a half-dollar on the floor and tried to stamp on it but it escaped.

To this dream, he associated the fact that the door was kept open when his little daughter was in the bathroom. Then he thought of his interest in his mother's buttocks when he was three years old. He wondered if he was currently angry at his wife. The rest of the hour was spent in voicing resentment at brother figures. In this dream, he was still dealing with the same elements of hostility to parental sexuality, typical of his analysis. But now he was aware that the spider, which he tried to stamp out in the dream, was associated with the half-dollar, the money, which had always been his means of taking potency away from men. In the dream, he felt able to take an aggressive step although it was still connected with an abortion fantasy. It was after this dream that he began to talk more freely about family relationships in his early childhood and recovered a forgotten memory of his father repeatedly coming to his mother's bed, a large double bed, next to his own. He also had a vague memory, from a few years later, of urinating on his sister, making her angry, so that she did the same to him—on the sister's bed which was then next to his. It was after this that more heterosexual urges began to come out, with incestuous objects and much conflict.

Such patients as these, latently homosexual or perverse, have maintained a rigid equilibrium within the superego and, when the balance breaks down, they develop symptoms and come to analysis. No sooner are they in analysis than many of these patients feel more relaxed and, consequently, resist gaining real insight. An overt confession of femininity may resemble a chess gambit in which, instead of a bishop or knight, the queen is moved forward to trap the opponent's king.

As a final example, it might be interesting to see how, in his analysis, a comparatively normal male patient used a sudden confession of his feminine tendencies as a diversionary tactic, to avoid dealing with strong hostility toward father figures. In the severely anxious personalities of overt homosexuals, interpretations of hostility in connection with homosexual impulses must proceed slowly and cautiously; where the homosexual aspect is mainly a defense of outward submissiveness, utilized to mask aggression, it is a matter of experience and timing to know when to make an interpretation of the hostility inherent in the basically heterosexual man's sporadic expressions of femininity. In the following example, although homosexuality was given clear expression, it was being utilized by the patient defensively, as a reaction to acutely mobilized masculine competition.

The patient saw the analyst driving a new car and mentioned, in the following hour, that he had had a very mild reaction to seeing it; it was the analyst's business if he wanted to get a new car, etc. These days people are all buying foreign sports cars, he observed, because everybody has new cars, and the buyers of new cars want to have something different. Then he wondered why the analyst had spent so much money on a car but added that that was the analyst's business. Over the weekend, this patient developed vague anxiousness about feminine tendencies. Toward the end of the week, he said he had developed anxiety in the course of business transactions with an effeminate man. Six days later, the patient talked freely about anxiety developing within himself and concluded that he had a real wish to have a female body and receive the male organ. Dealings with the effeminate business associate had made him anxious. He got control of himself and, after talking about this cause of his anxiousness, he felt better. Then he thought of a man from San Francisco, written up in the local newspapers, who wanted to be transformed into a woman, and another man who went to Europe for a similar operation. "American doctors are wrong not to do this for these people," he said. He was aware of a wish to be a woman and have all the characteristics of a woman. Next day he reported a dream:

> A friend of his, Jean, and Jean's wife and the patient and the patient's wife were together. Jean was showing them how he had worked out something typographical that prints on a large sheet. When the patient looked more closely, he saw a rabbit, a cat and some small rodent. He admired this and his own wife admired it, too, although not as much as he did.

His associations were that Jean is a machinist, a close friend, sensitive, with some anxiety and some latent homosexual tendencies, for which he had received psychotherapy. Jean once told him that, when he was a boy, he sold newspapers and his father would come by in his car and pick him up and buy all of his unsold newspapers. Jean said he supposed he would like to have somebody like his father do things for him. The patient had been sympathetic, because he, too, lacked a father and had always, in childhood, looked for a man to identify with, including his older brother. Then he thought of his anxiety about the homosexual man and the anxiety he had felt in the past about a brutal M.P., toward whom he had an urge to submit when in the army. At a business meeting the night before, he had noticed the big, strong wrists of one of his associates; he would like to be like that. But he was sure the others had problems also. Then he discussed his methods of handling anxiety in the past, how he tried to think of some strong person to identify with, like his brother, but the brother did not suffice. The other day, he thought of the analyst when he was anxious. He considered telephoning but then thought he could handle the anxiety himself.

When asked about the pictures of animals in the dream, he

thought of rabbits and his daughter's laughing at a name that sounded like "rabbit." When he was a small boy, a fellow he admired very much raised rabbits. This other boy was more courageous, more masculine. When the patient was at college in biology class, doing research on rabbits, the rabbits copulated. Although he knew that the female rabbit ovulates when having intercourse, the patient had always had the idea that somehow *the male rabbit's organ was clamped in the female and was injured and could not get out.* His association to cats was similar. He thought of cats howling during intercourse as if the male cat were injured in intercourse with the female and crying out.

A transference interpretation was made: "I think you are reacting to something you have discussed a good deal lately but denied being interested in, and that is seeing my new car. The machinist's invention and the boy selling papers and being helped by his father may be references to your business plans. An attitude of competitiveness for financial success seems to have aroused hostility toward me. That is handled by feminine identification, in which the male gets hurt, in your associations."

He replied, "Come to think of it, I saw you in that car again last night, I was driving just behind you. I don't know quite how to deal with this. My first reaction is that I am having sexual intercourse with you here."

He was told, "I think that confirms what I have been saying, it is in order that the car be taken away."

He understood how his masculine rivalry was stimulating a wish to damage the male. There was a sensation in his legs and some fear and uneasiness, he said.

"As if you felt retaliation for this impulse," he was told.

In the above hour, we had the beginning of the analysis of castration material, similar to mechanisms described by Freud in his paper on *Neurotic Mechanisms in Jealousy,* etc.[1] The patient's display of feminine wishes was, in this case, a thin disguise for competitive aggression, a bid for continued care from the father image. Mobilized aggression led to increased display of femininity. In a quite well-integrated individual, it was possible to utilize the illustration of his reaction to jealousy of the car in order to interpret the underlying aggression that prompted it. In this case, it ushered in the analysis of the rivalry with the father.

We have summarized, with the four condensed illustrations given above, some variations of two common and related themes: the close bond between submissiveness and aggression in homosexual impulses in the male and the inhibition of masculine identification in homosexuality. In female cases, a parallel mechanism may be observed, i.e., lack of identification with the mother and increased submissiveness and aggression toward her.

An attempt has been made here to show how the inability to identify with a powerful father involves the aggression-and-submission pattern, both as a reaction to frustration and as an expression of castration fear.

In the male cases to which I have drawn attention, homosexual submission was stimulated by whatever unconsciously or consciously stimulated competitiveness with the father. In the first case, inviting a girl to a concert; in the second case, expression of profound competitive hostility to the analyst; in the third, a financially castrative attitude which was being worked through in the transference; and, in the last, envy of the car which, to the patient, meant potency. Freud[1,2] initially described homosexual cases in which the erotization of the aggression was undisturbed. What I have attempted to demonstrate is the disturbance of this status—due to the analytic process in the cases described—and the manner in which aggression and submission tend to be stimulated together and to be given simultaneous expression. It is because these patients do not have a strong masculine identification that they have not worked out a submission-aggression pattern in a heterosexual direction which would, potentially, be more constructive. When an aggressive urge is stimulated, their identification is with the mother. The expression of strong aggression is through the medium of female identification—as in the vacuum cleaner dream, the dream of the scissors, or the black spider, or as, in the last case cited, the wish to be a woman. A submissive plea for parental care presents itself when rivalrous aggression against the father is stimulated. That is the reason the ambivalence is manifestly so intense and that is also the reason the submission-aggression pattern in male homosexuality is based on the absence of identification with a potent father.

Therapy

In therapy, insight into the relation between submission and aggression, as it is evoked in daily life, based originally on past patterns, was very helpful in such cases as the above, when homosexual trends were mobilized. Although it is very difficult to break up the homosexual submission-and-aggression pattern, in the first case cited (vacuum cleaner dream) insight enabled the patient to learn to exercise some control over his impulses. In other words, he had come to understand the aggression, based on Oedipal conflict, on which his submissive homosexuality was founded. This hospital employee was able to function in his job more effectively and at the same time to feel more actual anger at his colleagues. He could keep the anger under control, because he understood its derivation, its competitive source. Formerly, he had submitted compulsively, felt guilty, withdrawn, and turned to a homosexual outlet. He also had more understanding of his dread of any contact with women. The basic homosexual pattern is hard to eradicate, but insight into the conflicts crystallized around homosexuality is helpful in social adjustment; the latter then breaks up a vicious circle of guilt, withdrawal, failure and frustration— increasing aggression, increasing homosexual compulsive acting out and a feeling of hopelessness. When this pattern was partially replaced by actual insight and a certain ability to rise above it and discuss his behavior intelligently, he could control his impulses to some extent, though not totally. This particular patient, because of his improvement, was in a position to continue his career elsewhere. He did not finish his analysis which had reached a point where the pattern of his main conflicts was under more conscious control. He knew that, when he felt the urge to have a homosexual affair, it was because he was in a general state of angry rebellion; he also knew that he could face the latter, with its implications of past reactions to father and brother, as well as the mother-identification. He had worked through in the transference the relation between his rebellion and the submissive drives toward his father. He had come to anaylsis with the problem of depression, which was considerably relieved, and not with the hope of "curing" his homosexuality.

In the second case—an older man with a neurotic marriage and habitual alcoholism—the life situation was already deeply complicated, so that the extent of character change had to be measured by increased insight rather than by the reversal of fundamental character trends. The check upon an increasingly depressed and self-destructive trend was perhaps the chief accomplishment; it is difficult to estimate the actual result of the insight achieved, in so far as homosexual episodes in the future might be a reaction to frustrating circumstances.

The third patient, with the perversion, established more

harmonious relationships with family and business associates, and had freer sexual impulses on a normal basis; at times, however, perverse impulses recurred. He had a great deal more understanding of the relation between his attitude toward men in business, his feelings about his father and brothers, his ambivalent transference in the analysis, and the submissive, masochistic urges toward women which, in the past, had seemed so mysterious and yet so overpowering to him. He was able to establish much more successful relations with his children and to be a better father. Here, too, the sexual problem was not the cause of his seeking treatment; it was, nevertheless, at the root of his problems without his being cognizant of the fact.

The fourth, a comparatively normal patient, was able to work through castration-fear material after analysis of the submission-aggression urges in the transference centered about the "feminine" dream quoted.

The role of insight as a possible factor in actual reversal from overt homosexuality to heterosexuality would require further study. All that can be stressed here is that increased understanding of erotized, submissive homosexual impulses— as an unconscious reaction to aggression toward men and to hostile identification with the mother—can diminish the anxiety and some of the general symptomatology in homosexual men and enable them to carry on a more stabilized, satisfactory and socially useful existence.

Identification with the mother in these men is an early and rigid character defense, probably involving physiological functions in the pattern of growth and development, which become a nucleus of unconscious symbolisms and cognitive patterns that are firmly established from an early age; this is what makes the homosexual so difficult to "cure."

The physiology of the body is affected by both submissive and aggressive urges. The repression or over-stimulation of either may result in endocrinological changes, for example. And, from another angle, that of acting out, we have to consider the social and sociological implications. The relation of submission to aggression in homosexuality is by no means the whole story. I have stressed that particular aspect in this chapter because it seems to have been relatively neglected and because a consideration of it is pertinent to the treatment of homosexuality.

REFERENCES

1   Freud, Sigmund. "Neurotic Mechanisms in Jealousy, Paranoia and Homosexuality." *Coll. Papers,* Vol. II. London, 1924.

2   ———. *Three Contributions to the Theory of Sex.* New York, 1930.

3   Ferenczi, Sandor. "Nosology of Male Homosexuality." *Sex in Psychoanalysis.* N. Y., 1950.

4   ———. "On the Symbolism of the Head of Medusa." *Further Contributions.* London, 1926.

III

Sado-Masochism

Psychodynamic Theory of Masochism

BELA GRUNBERGER

Deux instincts sont en moi,
Vertige et déraison,
J'ai l'effroi du bonheur,
Et la soif du poison.
                    AMIEL[1]

I once had occasion to quote the above lines during a discussion of this subject with a friend and colleague. "Masochism!" he exclaimed. "Be careful. Amiel was a great obsessional."

Amiel was indeed an obsessional. Sacher-Masoch, the worthy godfather of masochism, was a hysteric. Nacht, in his important work on the subject,[26] demonstrates the part played by masochism in practically all psychopathology. Much importance is also attached to the role of masochism in the new field of psychosomatic medicine. Thus one comes across it everywhere. It transcends established clinical concepts, principally in two dimensions. In the first place, in the horizontal respect, we find it transcending the hysterical pattern, whether the latter is obsessional or not, and lying at the back of everything else; and in a way the same is true in a vertical respect, since masochism transcends and seems to be consubtantial with human

183

nature itself. (This observation might even be extended to three dimensions; in the course of treatment masochism often outlasts other symptoms, thus being transcendental in time also.) Certain writers, such as Reik[31] and Berliner,[5] have made investigations in this direction. Freud[14,18] refers on a number of occasions to non-neurotic masochists and to immanent masochism.

That offers a very tempting prospect and opens up large horizons but, in my opinion, it is inappropriate from the point of view of psychoanalytic research, the specific goal of which must be better knowledge of the neuroses and psychoses. Whether masochism appears in the guise of a neurotic tendency or morbid behavior, whether it be instinct or symptom, code of conduct or system of ethics or philosophy, we must seek to individualize it as rigorously as possible within the nosological framework and, for this purpose, we must circumscribe the phenomenon rather than expand it to infinity. Disengaging the "masochistic mechanism" with the precision desired will not only help us to a better knowledge of the masochism which dominates all human psychopathology but will also yield us information about the neuroses in general.

[II]

Those who concern themselves with "the famous and terrible problem of masochism" (Odier[28]) run the risk of being immediately attracted and fascinated by the paradoxical combination of pain and pleasure. Confronted with the strange phenomenon of the search for pain, the inquirer is tempted to concentrate on it, and this often leads him into reflections which are more speculative than clinical. Moreover, in this he will meet with eager co-operation on the part of his patients, who will obligingly supply him with material capable of being used for the setting up of hypotheses based, for example, on

narcissistic gratification. (Eidelberg[7]; Lampl de Groot.[21])
These, however, are rationalizations and, even if light can
be thrown on certain aspects of masochism by these methods,
the clarifications thus obtained cannot be considered satisfactory. We shall therefore renounce pain as the point of
departure for our investigations and concentrate our attention
on the pleasure element instead.

We know that, apart from searching out pain, the masochist
is characterized by total inhibition in the face of pleasure,
pleasure of every kind. This is a point to which we shall return.
In his chapter on the masochistic character, Nacht[26] draws
attention to the inability to enjoy pleasures of life as a typical
masochistic character trait. He mentions this last of all. To
my way of thinking, however, it seems the most important
feature. (Without wishing to insist on the point here, it seems
to me that the masochist's incapacity to enjoy pleasure extends
to all the phases of instinctual gratification, both genital and
pregenital. Beneath this incapacity, however, there exists a
strong wish to achieve pleasure all the same. It is this that
causes the patient to accept analysis, and, in some measure,
it is the presence of a masochistic element in every neurosis
which causes the patient to submit to analysis and continue
with it to a successful conclusion.) The masochist pursues
pleasure, which he, like everyone else, desires. He even desires
it—as is, indeed, only natural—more than other people do,
as is proved by his conscious and unconscious life in its most
diverse manifestations. It is at the moment of achieving
pleasure, at the moment of taking a decisive, even if indirect,
step toward it, that he recoils. He recoils from the anxiety
which invariably arises in the presence of the pleasure-object,
no matter in what form the latter appears, and returns to his
former position, which is not one of renunciation pure and

simple but of the opposite of pleasure, namely unpleasure. Without entering more deeply into details, we can conclude that what has been achieved by this is the disappearance of anxiety.

Various authors—Reik,[31] for instance—have drawn attention to the avoidance of anxiety in masochism. But, to my way of thinking, Reik's theory does not take the mechanism of masochistic pleasure sufficiently into account. Lewinsky[23] writes of masochism as the negation of anxiety but puts forward no solution for the problem as a whole.

> The masochist Waldemar led a dangerous life, full of difficulties and privations, which he bore perfectly well. His mental and physical health left little to be desired. The masochist mechanism worked smoothly and without friction until the day when, by a fortunate and extraordinary combination of circumstances, he found himself face to face with a business opportunity which called for no effort on his part but would bring a fortune his way involving a complete change in his material circumstances. No sooner did he realize this than he was seized with anxiety, which grew until it became intolerable, reaching a point at which he felt an imperious need to do something immediately to rid himself of the opportunity, which he accordingly declined. That done, he breathed freely again, returned to his former situation, and resumed his old life. What a relief! He had had a narrow shave, had escaped by the skin of his teeth.

Can we say that Waldemar was searching for pain and finding pleasure in it? It does not seem so. He simply turned his back on pleasure in order to seek shelter from anxiety. If we insist on the pleasure element, it is because Waldemar's privations were not absolute. He had a sexual life and was able to enjoy mediocre, more or less "de-hedonized" gratifications. But, at the slightest attempt to cross the threshold which separated him from rich and genuine instinctual gratifications, anxiety made its implacable appearance. Generally, he unconsciously managed his life in such a way that this dangerous threshold was never reached, and all the dangerous drives in that direction were kept well repressed. Only analysis could release them and the anxiety associated with them. But, in everyday life, the anxiety remained more or less latent. In the neurosis of failure only the failure is evident and, in mental masochism, only the pain.

[III]

With anxiety, we touch on the core of the masochistic problem and the much debated question of the fear of castration as a motivation of masochistic behavior. (Nacht[26] says: "Everything happens as if the masochist, faced with the danger of losing everything, consents to the sacrifice of a part to save the rest.") However, I think it useless to resume this discussion again in detail though I do not propose to ignore it entirely. Actually, it throws a certain light on the solution of the problem of masochism as I foresee it.

Let me explain. Observation of a patient shows us that, during a certain phase of the analysis, there occur two parallel developments which sometimes, however, take place independently of each other. On the one hand, the patient abreacts his anxiety. We shall not examine the development of this abreaction here, for it would take us far from our subject. We shall say, however, that in general it all takes place in silence, the anxiety being by definition experienced as being non-objectual. On the other hand, the patient periodically shows us his castration complex, and does so with a certain ostentation, to state it no more strongly than that. These manifestations can be dramatic but often remain on a superficial level and obviously serve the purpose of display. During this period, there is not the slightest trace of real anxiety. On the contrary, the patient may adopt an amused tone which may extend to outright hilarity. This is not a defense but the whole complex functioning as a (temporarily successful) defense against anxiety. Here is a lapidary statement made by one of my patients, a masochistic obsessional:

> "I have only to wish for some part of my body to be cut off, and then I have no more anxiety."

A young woman who made her husband beat her during sexual intercourse complained of frigidity and, in particular, of extremely severe attacks of anxiety. After three months' analysis, her anxiety ceased. A dream coinciding with the improvement, and accompanied by transference material having similar significance, shows us the same device, with the active participation of the superego:

> "I was in a sanatorium, talking to another young woman and trying to convince her that I had a cavity. In fact I knew that I had no cavity, but maintained the opposite. She said that my condition was not serious, and that irritated me."
>
> *Associations:* "I was among the least seriously ill in the sanatorium, but nobody was as tired as I was. I should have liked to tell everyone: 'You see, I am ill,' etc."

The masochistic pervert's *mise-en-scène* and all the self-castration material appearing in the masochist's dreams, phantasies and real life present the same picture. Freud[17] says that "the tortures of the masochist rarely appear as serious as the cruelties of the sadist." Feldman describes sado-masochistic regression as hypocritical. Loewenstein[8,24] rejects this term and prefers to talk of "play" and "make-believe." We are confronted with a defense system *en bloc,* and Reik[31] understood as much when he said that the fear of castration, as it appears in masochism, is itself masochism, and that one should not set out to explain a phenomenon by the phenomenon itself.

In any case, there is nothing specific about the fear of castration, as is pointed out by Berliner.[5] On the contrary, interpreting what has gone before, I believe the specific feature of masochism to be the utilization for defensive purposes, in a factitious and ostentatory manner, of a way of behavior that is genuine in itself, e.g., the fear of castration.

[IV]

I have glanced at the relationship between masochism and the fear of castration (on the genital level) in order to show that, as the explanation of masochism, it has led us into an *impasse*. If we turn to the pregenital phase, we notice immediately that much recourse has been had to orality to explain the genesis of masochism. It would be tedious to mention all the authors who have referred to oral conflict in this connection. However, we cannot omit mention of Bergler,[3] for whom there exists only one neurosis, the "basic neurosis," the sole manifestation of which is moral masochism. He regards this as deriving from oral conflict, the other neuroses being only "rescue stations" in which relief may be had from it. Rado[29] has attempted to build a whole theory of neurosis on masochism, starting out from the oral stage. Nacht[26,27] arrives at the conception of a "biological masochism" originating in the earliest pregenital phase, the pre-objectual phase during which the infant does not distinguish between its own body and its mother's breast. For the adherents of the theory of orality, masochism is a kind of recrudescence of oral frustration, and Bergler[3] even speaks of the desire to be frustrated. This frustration in itself would be a source of pleasure. Finally, in the view of Berliner,[5] the child identifies itself with the frustrating object, fixation on the wicked mother being the only way in which the child can be loved, there being historical reasons for this which can be verified in analysis.

Without entering into a detailed examination of these theories, the following criticisms may be made:

1. Those who support theories which derive masochism from oral conflict and frustration seem to take no account of the fact that masochism is, by definition, related above all to the anal-sadistic phase. Freud[9,12,16,10] always considered masochism to be the counterpart of sadism and firmly expressed his conviction that a solution of the problem of masochism could be attained only by way of sadism, the two being inseparable. Nacht's important contribution[26] to the study of masochism tends in the same direction. His taking the factor of aggression into account appears to me to be an important and decisive step toward the solution of this thorny problem.

2. Certain clinical objections can be made to the hypothesis of a purely oral genesis of masochism as envisaged, for instance, by W. Reich[30]: "The masochist always pursues pleasure, but invariably runs into frustration."

Freud himself was surprised to note[15] that the children who produced this phantasy ("a child is being beaten") had, so to speak, never been physically maltreated. Masochists are, in fact, mostly recruited from the ranks of spoiled children, a fact which is so obvious that Esther Menaker[25] used it as a point of departure for a theory of masochism. According to her, masochists were children who, because of lack of repeated oral frustrations, were unable sufficiently to reinforce their ego, this weakness of the ego constituting the frustration. Karen Horney[19] has argued that the masochist, in order to avoid anxiety, partly abandons his ego, keeping it weak, this being felt by him to be his only safeguard. Reik[31] once drew attention to the readiness with which women psychoanalysts in particular tended to consider female masochism as almost biological.

This observation leads me to repeat in connection with oral conflict what I have said in connection with the castration complex. The masochist uses it in the same way, and probably for the same purpose. The clinical material shows indeed that the patient gladly produces stories of oral frustration taken from his past life, just as in his present life and in his analysis he insists on playing the role of victim. One should therefore be extremely cautious before asserting the importance of oral frustration as a primary element in the history of the masochistic individual, as Keiser[20] does. ("In my observations, masochists have invariably had castrating mothers.") I recall a woman masochist whose whole analysis unfolded under the sign of a castrating mother and a weak and disappointing father. This situation was abundantly described and illustrated until the day came when we realized that this picture had been exaggerated for the purpose of reducing the patient's guilt, in accordance with the formula: "It was not I who castrated my father but my mother, who castrated me as well."

A young man, who was being analyzed, produced clinical material from which it emerged indisputably that in infancy he had been the victim of severe alimentary frustration. The patient produced a series of dreams and phantasies all converging toward a definite point which, in the end, it was possible to interpret as the "memory" of having been poisoned by his mother's milk. The fact that his mother had, in reality, had an abscess of the breast seemed to be a confirmation of this. But further investigation brought to light the fact that the abscess had occurred when his mother was nursing his brother, his junior by three years, and that his own nursing period had apparently passed off without trouble.

Apart from those patients who "come out with" their maternal conflict after a period generally devoted to their Oedipus conflict, there are some who produce it very quickly and even come to analysis with an open, violent and often actual maternal conflict. They insist on it at great length and with much freedom and evident satisfaction, and would like nothing better than to go on talking about it throughout the analysis. It is sometimes difficult to distinguish between the real, historical oral conflict and that deliberately put forward by the patient in order to mask something else.

Sometimes the process that takes place at the beginning or during the course of an analysis takes on an even clearer aspect toward the end or, rather, what should be the end of the analysis. At this stage, the patient makes a desperate effort to prevent the analyst from bringing the analysis to a successful conclusion. This appears in the form of a particularly tough resistance, manifesting itself in a sudden and violent reawakening of the oral conflict which one believed had been liquidated. This development is well adapted to make analysts despair, for it conjures up the "interminable analysis" bogy—all the more because the patient reacts to every new step taken by the analyst to bring the analysis to an end as a new oral frustration and responds to it all the more violently because that frustration serves as an excuse. Thus we find ourselves in a vicious circle which it is necessary to break.

[v]

The castration complex and the oral conflict exhaust the phenomenology of masochism. In life, as in analysis, all the specific aspects of masochistic behavior come within the framework of these two factors. The masochist, above all, arranges his life in such a way as to be castrated, that is to say, in such a way as to be incapable of pleasure in any field whatever; he is inhibited, poor, suffering, sick, diminished, "offended and humiliated." All these symptoms are negations of gratifications. Thus a young woman whom I treated for frigidity said to me that she considered her inability to have an orgasm as a shame to be concealed and a humiliation and, in her dreams, this humiliation took the form of castration. It may also be observed that the masochist frequently revives his oral conflict, with a grudge against his mother or mother-substitutes, these terms being understood in their functional sense, of course. His manifest complaints, to which he gives expression in a vindictive tone, show him in the light of a victim: no one likes him, he is treated badly, he has no luck, he is a victim of injustice. Whether he says so or not, the specifically masochistic part of his behavior is a never-ending demonstration of this state of affairs, a double demonstration with but a single purpose. Certainly this behavior appears equivocal and even paradoxical at times, as, in the very process of complaining (e.g., in analysis), he manages to exasperate his interlocutor, with the obvious purpose of provoking his rejection by the latter. His behavior becomes intelligible, however, if one considers that he is addressing himself to two figures at once, the mother and the father. The provocative attitude is intended to induce ill-treatment by the former, while the demonstration of what is taking place is directed at the latter. In the last resort, it is the frustrating mother who is the source of all the rejections, privations and ill-treatment of which the patient feels himself to be the victim, whether the ill-treatment is handed out by his love-partner or by his employer, by society or by God, by the stars or by the universe as a whole; and all the sufferings which she inflicts on the masochist are displayed for the benefit of the father. The masochist's ever-present interlocutor, whether real or imaginary, is a condensation of the mother and father figures. In analysis, there are three *dramatis personae*, two of whom are represented by the analyst, and the formula is not so much "Look what you are doing to me" as "Look how badly *she* treats me." We are confronted with a pre-Oedipal conflict, the object of which is not erotic rivalry with the parent of the same sex. The enemy is always the frustrating mother; the father plays a different role, to which we shall return. In studying the phantasies and *mise-en-scènes* of masochistic beating, one realizes that it is always the mother who does the beating, either overtly (in the case of men) or in disguise (in the case of women). In the latter's the man's role is often a humiliating attitude of indifference or neglect—a dramatized form of frustration imposed by the mother. The blows express coercion in the sense: "You will not do what you want to do unless forced to by me; that shows that you cannot attain your gratification of your own free will—you are castrated." There is, however, one striking detail in beating phantasies (a detailed analysis of which cannot be given here) which is, moreover, in accordance with Freud's observation that the phase in which the child is beaten by the father is very frequently repressed and can be brought to light only by analytic investigation. (In the exceptional cases in which the beating is done overtly by the father, we are probably confronted with less inhibited subjects who are content with a single defense: "It is he who is the castrator, and not I.") The woman who beats the masochistic pervert has male elements in her special attire (which is always the same, and is adapted to the affective position at an archaic level). Thus it is a condensed object which does the beating. But its masculine opponent nearly always has to remain unconscious. In this connection, Reik[31] reports a very characteristic case: during a masochist *mise-en-scène*, a patient discovered in his partner's attire something which reminded him of his father's beard. The erotic character of the scene vanished entirely and orgasm became impossible. How shall we interpret this incident?

We have seen that the content of the masochist's attitude is, on the one hand, being castrated and, on the other, being frustrated by the mother, his aim being the permanent demonstration of this state of affairs. Everything leads us to believe that the masochist cannot renounce this behavior which protects him from something that seems to him intolerable and, at the same time, blocks his path toward the gratification of his instinctual drives. Before trying to arrive at a general view of the situation, let us return to the phantasy of being beaten. Why must the paternal imago so often remain repressed and why is its unexpected emergence fatal in these cases to the success of the masochistic *mise-en-scène*? Purely and simply because the sole purpose of the whole masochistic structure is to maintain the repression. Freud[17] says that observation of the masochistic beating phantasy creates the impression that its subject has done something reprehensible (the nature of which is entirely vague) for which he must be punished. Our clinical material enables us to assert that, in all cases of masochism of every kind, we are confronted with castration of the father as an indispensable condition of gratification of the instinctual drive, and this in both sexes. The masochistic mechanism consists of a defense against this drive which, nevertheless, permits it to pursue and achieve its aim in a changed and disguised fashion which we shall describe later; and this aim is the castration of the father. In the course of analysis, one always discovers, behind the masochistic defense, the more or less disguised desire for and achievement of this castration or, rather, the introjection of the paternal penis in an anal-sadistic manner.

One of my patients, whose history will be told later, de-

veloped in the transference some reactions very characteristic
of the masochistic mechanism revolving round the question
of payment of fees. One day he handed me a check which, by
mistake, he had made out for an excessive amount (simulated
self-castration). Moreover, his bank balance was insufficient
to meet the check. For days afterwards, he tormented himself
on the subject. "Whenever I think of that check," he said, "I
feel as if you were turning a knife in my heart. You have a
weapon against me in your pocket." (In the meantime, I had
returned to him the excess amount he had paid me and was
waiting before presenting the check.) But he was forced to
admit that, every time he planned to go to the bank to put
the matter in order, he was prevented from doing so. When
I drew his attention to the castration that he was inflicting on
me, he was astonished but also said that, since his mistake,
he had never been so potent sexually.

This distinction between the Oedipal murder of the father
and the pregenital castration is very important. Actually, it
seems that this introjection has to precede the transition to
the Oedipal level which takes another phenomenological
course. The victory over the father, his elimination as a rival
on the Oedipal plane, cannot be superimposed on his sadistic
castration which, moreover, is directed at a part-object's becoming a total object only by extension. In certain analyses,
one observes that the reliving of the Oedipal combat and its
interpretation awaken no opposition in the patient while, if
he is shown the sadistic destruction of the paternal penis, he
puts up the fiercest resistance. Killing of the father is acceptable, but not his castration; possession of his penis, but not
its destruction. These *nuances* are important. Another proof
that we are on the pregenital plane is the fact that the sadistic
introjection in question is obligatory in both sexes and rouses

greater guilt in women than in men. Behind the masochistic defense picture, the castration of the father in this sense is always present, though sometimes very much disguised.

Vincent dreamed that he saw, at a hotel window, a seductive young woman dressed in a gossamer nightgown. He went to look for her but lost his way in a succession of rooms. The search was very harrowing and painful. Vincent was assisted in his search by a number of male hotel employees. These were very helpful, were dressed in green (an allusion to my name), and were short in stature. Their help was vain, however, and they looked at Vincent with pity.

The situation was clear. Vincent was demonstrating to his superego—the analyst—that he considered himself castrated (unable to achieve pleasure) and that it was the woman (the inaccessible mother) who frustrated him. His friendly relations with the hotel men (the analyst) ill concealed the castration which he inflicted on them. The analyst is a hotel employee, short in stature and incapable of finding the way to the mother. (At a deeper level, the woman also represents the paternal penis.)

Otto came to analysis in an aggressive mood, complaining that he got nothing from me and that his analysis was getting nowhere (i.e., he remained castrated). He also said: "It's cold here [lack of maternal warmth]." Later he told me that he had seen a man's hairy arm in a café and had felt a desire to kiss it. "So, you see, you're not curing me." I showed him that he was castrating me and he replied immediately: "That's true. I've often thought that kissing is biting, cutting." Then he went on, without any transition, "I'm a little boy. My mother is beating me."

Véronique, aged forty, came to analysis because of various psychosomatic disorders; the picture, however, was rather of a failure neurosis. The first few months of analysis were devoted to an *exposé* at great length of a sharp and permanent conflict between her and her mother. She accepted the Oedipal interpretations without resistance, and even with obvious pleasure. But things changed on the day the positive transference produced anxiety as well as a new symptom, dysmenorrhoea. Her periods became painful and of abnormal duration. She complained bitterly of this and of the social injustice which made women "eter-

nal victims." At one session, she delivered an onslaught on male
prerogatives and produced a dream in which she saw herself
during analysis bathing in her own blood and soiling the couch.
Associations led her to talk about a film of Menotti's, *The
Medium*, and she insisted on the tragic fate of the "victim," i.e.,
the principal woman character. Now, in the film, this woman kills
a young boy, a fact which the patient completely obscured from
herself; she was dumfounded when I reminded her of the fact.
Shaken by this flash of insight, she produced material from
which it emerged that she attributed a phallic significance to the
real victim in the film, a black, semi-nude deaf-mute who was
the playmate of the heroine's daughter. She further realized the
anal-aggressive significance of her dream and, also, why her
dysmenorrhoea regularly coincided with monthly complications
about paying me my fee when it was due, the meaning of which
was my castration. All this was followed by a massive emergence
of memories relating to her impulses to castrate her father in an
anal-sadistic fashion, as well as a number of similar phantasies.

Juliette, a journalist, aged twenty-eight, suffered from a complicated and atypical neurosis for which she had already been treated
by another analyst. Analysis brought about a slow but definite
improvement but she produced many acts of self-castration and
had a great deal of difficulty in "coming out with" her positive
transference. Actually, she seemed to be making a "transference
dichotomy," reserving the positive side of the latter for her
previous analyst whom, however, she persistently accused of
having abandoned her. Being in possession of material which I
cannot report here, I told her point-blank that her complaints
about the other analyst, who represented her mother, enabled
her more easily to castrate her father, that is to say, me. The
effect of this intervention was dramatic. "I see your eyes, they
are the eyes of my father, the eyes of an old man who is going
to die," she said. "I am independent, and my father is old and
helpless." Then, sobbing, she went on: "As he goes down, I go
up. How could I love you, as I think only of your death?"

When she came next day she said: "You have entered into my
analysis. I dreamed about you personally." The dream is too long
to be reproduced here. She was mistaken in her comment, however, because she had had similar dreams before but had forgotten them immediately. But she identified herself with this

dream and her transference attitude turned out to have been profoundly modified by this incident.

The typical masochistic elements appeal in all this material:
1. Self-castration.
2. Frustration by the bad mother and identification with her.
3. Both concealing castration of the father.

[vi]

We have seen that masochism is a defense mechanism which enables the ego to mystify the superego. The object is to mask the wish to possess the paternal penis, in other words, to incorporate it in a sadistic manner. The defense mechanism expresses two things:

1. "I do not wish to castrate my father and, in any case, I could not, as I am castrated myself (I am castrated by my mother)."

2. "If I am in conflict, it is with my mother (and not with my father); the conflict is an oral conflict."

The structure of the defense may be different. One of my patients tried to prove:

1. That it was the analyst who was castrating her.
2. That it was the analyst (and not she) who was castrating her husband.
3. That it was the analyst's wife (and not she) who was castrating the analyst.

Since the masochist's behavior is an attempt to relieve himself from guilt, we can understand the role played in his life by pain, the architect of this relief from guilt. For the moral masochist, suffering is not a sacrifice accepted for the sake of achieving pleasure; he never achieves it. For the same reason, it is even less self-punishment. Nevertheless, the masochist considers suffering as having value, and sometimes it is the only value that he admits. (In this overevaluation of suffering, there is evidently a revival of the pleasure which it is supposed to repress; there is thus, to some extent, a return of the repressed under the mantle of the repressing forces.) It can be said that pain takes the place of pleasure; deep analysis reveals that it stands for the introjected penis—exactly like the whip of the masochistic pervert. It is only the level of introjection that is different; it is this which changes the character of the pleasure achieved.

Suffering ennobles and purifies. He who suffers is entitled to veneration for he is virtuous. Pleasure, indeed, being assimilated to castration of the father, it follows that suffering—i.e., being the castrated instead of the castrator—is a proof of innocence and a shelter against the accusations of the superego while, at the same time, permitting introjection at a deeper level. (I once overheard two women exchanging courtesies; one said to the other, with the air of granting her a diploma: "Of course I suffer, but what is my suffering compared with yours?" The diploma is the possession of the paternal penis. Those who suffer are proud of it and we know that the inmates of sanatoria look down on the healthy. A "fakir" once said: "When I suffer, I'm afraid of nobody.") This suffering is utilized, measured out, varied or stabilized, its intensity corresponding exactly to the amount of the fear to be neutralized by this technique. In analysis, we often observe patients who display their castration to the last, though they have been surreptitiously getting better all the time. They suffer and act castration just like the beggar who, sitting all day behind a placard with the word "blind" on it, goes home and reads the newspaper. I remember a young man who castrated himself from morning to night. I explained to him how, behind the mask of this behavior, he was managing to castrate me. No apparent change took place in him. But imagine my astonishment when I learned that this inhibited, impotent young man, who had led a completely parasitical existence, after breaking off the analysis ostensibly for financial reasons had started working successfully and now had a wife and child.

This also enables us to understand one of the most important aspects of masochism, namely, projection. For we observe that the masochist has constantly to provoke the object in order to project his own aggression on to him. He constantly puts himself in the position of a victim, according to the formula: "It is you who are castrating me" (i.e., "It is not I who am aggressive, but you."). Thus in the case of the masochist, we are confronted not, as Nacht[26] says, with a turning in of aggression against the self but with a projection of aggression on to the object. This projection is typical of the masochist. Freud[15] mentioned that, one day, it might be possible to classify masochism under the heading of paranoia. What is it the masochist projects, and on to whom? We have seen that the drive to be projected is that toward the anal castration of the father. The recipient of the projection is the mother, for reasons to which we shall return. Thus it is the bad mother who castrates the father and retains his penis. (Kleinian conception of the pregenital interpretation of sexual relations, as set forth by Lebovici and Diatkine[22].) To obtain this penis, the masochist would have to introject the bad mother, therefore identifying himself with her. Berliner[5] thinks that the masochist seeks to carry out this identification in order to be loved and indicates that the type of masochist he was studying was the moral masochist. But the characteristic of the moral masochist is that he is unable to make this identification, for, if he were, he would not be a masochist but a sadist. The whole conduct of the moral masochist is characterized by a desperate and constant effort to prove to his superego that he is incapable of this identification and takes good care never to attempt it. All pleasure being subject to this condition, the masochist's reaction to it is always the same, namely, projection of the aggressive-sadistic component which endangers the paternal penis and consequently himself. This component has to be disposed of because of the unbearable anxiety it would provoke. It is as if the masochist, when brought face to face with pleasure—the good object—releases a trigger-mechanism, as it were, in order to find himself instead confronted with displeasure—the bad mother. But, as his instinctual drives demand satisfaction and are always present, he has continually to go through the same motion, day and night —as is proved by his dreams—in order to be able to live sheltered from anxiety. It is the need to pursue this projection continuously which forces him to live in suffering. It is not a simple inhibition but a display ("Look how she treats me!") and pleasure has automatically to become unpleasure. In the analyses and dreams of masochists, we invariably discover, behind the suffering, wishes of which it is the negation, the process being a strictly symmetrical one. The display is carried out in a logical manner, and the negative of success can only be failure, of happiness unhappiness, of health illness, of activity passivity, of triumph humiliation, and of the wish to castrate self-castration. One of my patients coined a phrase which summed it up. "I suffer from an opposite complex," he said.

In connection with the fear of identification with the bad mother we can quote Bergler.[4] He describes a masochistic husband who was completely put out and reduced to a state of terrible bewilderment and anxiety when, in response to his masochistic provocation—which Bergler considers "pseudo-aggressive"—his wife showed herself to be greatly hurt. Bergler's observation, which coincides with my own but is differently interpreted by him, seems to show the correctness of my point of view. The husband faced with this situation realizes that, though he has done all he can to demonstrate the opposite, his identification with the wicked mother has come about in spite of himself, so to speak. The result is that he founders in a sea of anxiety.

Here is a rather complicated case which is significant in this respect. It concerns a masochist who was deceived and badly treated by his wife (wicked mother). "My wife deceives and abuses me but that reassures me," he said. ("She is the wicked mother, not I.") He went on: "I ask her when she was last with her lover. 'At five-fifteen this afternoon,' she says. I become very excited, have an erection, and a very satisfactory coitus. I have the impression that, in telling me this, my wife is delivering the man up to me." (Castration of the father by identification with the mother in the guise of self-castration —he is the deceived husband.) "I have a feeling of superiority to the man, and am free from anxiety. But if my wife is difficult and argues and denies and I have to squabble with her, force her to confess [identification with the bad mother], I have heartbeats, feel anxiety and my erection subsides."

This apparently homosexual position (thanks to a large amount of transference material which lack of space prevents me from presenting) was analyzed as a defense against the desire to castrate the father in an anal-sadistic manner, and made possible transition to a most manifest Oedipal level. This shows that the homosexual attitudes of masochists are also projections on to the mother of the wish to castrate the father.

[VII]

What emerges from all this material is that the masochist can obtain pleasure when the introjection of the paternal penis has succeeded. This takes us back to the beginning of this discussion when we said that the masochist pursued his goal, reaching it or not according to circumstances. The goal is the castration of the father and, as the masochist has to carry out a preliminary identification with the bad mother to achieve this on the anal-sadistic level, the masochistic mechanism functions like a screen to conceal this identification. That is how the superego is deceived.

There are thus two kinds of masochists (with the whole range of mixed types in between):

1. Those who continue the diversionary maneuver as a defense against anxiety without ever achieving pleasure. These are the moral masochists.

2. Those who achieve their goal and obtain pleasure, orgasm, behind the protection of the masochistic mechanism. These are the masochistic perverts; and, provisionally, we must put in this category all those who seem to buy pleasure by what is generally and erroneously considered to be self-punishment.

Its fraudulent nature is demonstrated by the fact that, in extreme cases, a purely symbolic act is sufficient. I knew a woman masochist who had an orgasm every time she knelt. The ways in which masochists behave to attain their desired aim are very various, and the extent of the scale, which stretches from real pain on the one hand to a symbolic gesture on the other, is a function of the variations in strength and weakness of the ego in relation to the strength or weakness of the superego.

As for the moral masochist, he follows his path with less good fortune, but with all the more determination for that reason. Nothing will divert him from his goal, which is pleasure too. He is convinced that, one day, he will achieve it and the more he suffers, the sweeter will be his reward. Time does not exist for the unconscious and neither does death.

In analysis, the masochist behaves in the same fashion, with the difference that he learns to integrate his aggression and to overcome the obstacle which lies in its way. For this, it seems necessary for him to realize the identification with the wicked mother under the protection of its projection on to the analyst. That done, the introjection of the paternal penis —thanks to his released and normalized aggression—takes place on a level untainted with sadism. This, to use Bouvet's term,[8] is a "preservative introjection," the dynamic contribution which makes possible a transition to the Oedipal situation and its resolution.

Thus, at the root of masochism, we find dynamic disturbances which, though they originated, as always, in the oral period, did not really become pathogenic until the anal period because of the obstacles preventing the integration of the aggression which is so violently sought after at that stage. (If the spark is struck on the oral ground floor, the specific inflammable material is on the floor above.)

If it were a question of an oral conflict in the true sense of the term, we should find ourselves faced with specifically oral disorders, such as melancholia, depressive neuroses and psychoses, toxicomania, hysteria, etc. This point requires some clarification but I do not think I can embark on it here. Thanks to the clinical material, it seems to me sufficiently established:

1. That the introjection of the paternal penis is indispensable before Oedipal development can begin; this applies to both sexes.

2. That the disorder known as masochism indicates a disturbance of this process. The masochist is at grips with a dynamic problem and, to find a solution of his problem, we must abandon the libidinal framework and resolutely enter a dynamic framework, while keeping the role of the historic

factor to a strict minimum. That is what I have attempted to do, being convinced that a distinct orientation in that direction represents assured progress.

Conclusion

I have omitted a number of the aspects in which masochism is so rich and which have in any case, been partially studied elsewhere; instead, I have made an attempt to establish the mechanism invariably to be found in masochism which, to my mind, can be regarded as specific of this disorder. This mechanism is as follows:

1. It is an ego defense aimed at persuading the superego that instinctual gratification has been renounced. This instinctual gratification is bound up with castration of the father and is denied by proof of its opposite in accordance with the formula:

(a) It is I who am castrated, not my father.

(b) My conflict brings me into conflict with my mother and not with my father.

2. This defense position is reinforced by constant projection on to the bad mother of the wish to castrate the father. The masochist simultaneously makes a display of wishing to maintain this projection, thus demonstrating his refusal to identify himself with the bad mother.

3. Behind the cover of these defense mechanisms, the moral masochist pursues his goal—which is castration of the father by anal-sadistic introjection—but consistently demonstrates his failure.

The masochistic pervert, thanks to the masochistic disguise, succeeds in deceiving his superego in the most complete and glaring manner and thus achieves genital pleasure.

REFERENCES

1   Amiel, H. F. *Fragments d'un Journal Intime*. Paris, 1922.

2   Bak, R. "Masochism in Paranoia." *Psychoanalytic Quarterly*, Vol. XV, 1946.

3   Bergler, E. *The Basic Neurosis*. New York, 1949.

4   ———. "Neurotic Helplessness in 'the Masochistic Situation in Reverse.'" *Psychiatric Quarterly*, Vol. XXI, 1947.

5   Berliner, B. "On Some Psychodynamics of Masochism." *Psychoanalytic Quarterly*, Vol. XVI, 1947.

6   Bouvet, M. "Le moi dans la névrose obsessionelle." *Revue Francaise de Psychanalyse*, 1953.

7   Eidelberg, L. "Zur Metapsychologie des Masochismus." *Internationale Zeitschrift für Psychoanalyse*, Vol. XIX, 1933.

8   Feldman, S. "Anxiety and Orgasm." *Psychoanalytic Quarterly*, Vol. XX, 1951.

9   Freud, Sigmund. *Three Essays on the Theory of Sexuality*. London, 1949.

10 ———. "Instincts and their Vicissitudes." *Coll. Papers*, Vol. IV. London, 1924.

11 ———. "Some Character Types met with in Psychoanalytic Work." *Coll. Papers*, Vol. IV. London, 1924.

12 ———. *Introductory Lectures on Psychoanalysis*. New York, 1920.

13 ———. *New Introductory Lectures on Psychoanalysis*. New York, 1933.

14 ———. "From the History of an Infantile Neurosis." *Coll. Papers*, Vol. III. London, 1924.

15 ———. "A Child Is Being Beaten." *Coll. Papers*, Vol. II. London, 1924.

16 ———. *Beyond the Pleasure Principle*. London, 1922.

17 ———. "The Economic Problem in Masochism." *Coll. Papers*, Vol. II. London, 1924.

18   ———. "Dostoievsky and Parricide." *Coll. Papers,* Vol. V. London, 1950.

19   Horney, K. "The Problem of Feminine Masochism." *Psychoanalytic Review,* Vol. XVIII, 1935.

20   Keiser, S. "The Fear of Sexual Passivity in the Masochist." *International Journal of Psychoanalysis,* Vol. XXX, 1949.

21   Lampl–De Groot, J. "Masochismus und Narcissmus." *Internationale Zeitschrift für Psychoanalyse,* Vol. XXII, 1936.

22   Lebovici and Diatkine. "Étude des fantasmes chez l'enfant." *Revue francaise de Psychanalyse,* 1954.

23   Lewinsky, H. "On Some Aspects of Masochism." *International Journal of Psychoanalysis,* Vol. XXV, 1944.

24   Loewenstein, R. "L'origine du masochisme et la théorie des pulsions." *Revue francaise de Psychanalyse,* 1938.

25   Menaker, E. "Masochism—A Defense Reaction of the Ego." *Psychoanalytic Quarterly,* Vol. XXII, 1953.

26   Nacht, S. "Le masochisme." *Revue francaise de Psychanalyse,* 1938.

27   ———. "Essai sur la peur." *Ibid.,* 1952.

28   Odier, C. *L'homme esclave de son infériorité.* Paris.

29   Rado, S. "Fear of Castration in Women." *Psychoanalytic Quarterly,* Vol. II, 1933.

30   Reich, W. "Der masochistische Charakter." *Internationale Zeitschrift für Psychoanalyse,* Vol. XVIII, 1932.

31   Reik, T. *Le masochisme.* Paris.

The Analysis of a Sado-Masochist

GERHARD RUFFLER

I. PREHISTORY

The patient was thirty-eight, single, and was employed in a commercial enterprise.

Closer (Sexual) Symptomatology

The patient had no desire for normal coitus. He felt everything feminine to be dangerous to him. His real sexual object was the beating of nearly naked women on their bare buttocks. It was important that the woman should wear a red jersey and a tight brassière which emphasized her breasts; sometimes, particularly in his phantasies, he liked the picture to be completed by her wearing red slippers and black stockings. He also liked the scene to be introduced by the woman's wearing woolen bathing drawers. He then put himself into the role of a person in authority, rightfully and partially to his own distress, punishing the woman for some transgression so that, the requirements of justice having been fulfilled, a proper reconciliation would be possible. The patient did all this with a bad conscience because, though his partner might tolerate it, it gave her no satisfaction. He, therefore, felt himself under an obligation, though

the impulse was entirely lacking, to proceed to have intercourse with her but was unable to do so because of impotence.
During the process, he had an erection but no orgasm; he could
obtain orgasm only by masturbation accompanied by beating
phantasies, in which woman as genitally desired object did not
appear. He sought the physical proximity of women but only
for the exchange of tendernesses, in which he sought to play a
purely passive role, to be the beloved child.

Further Symptomatology

The patient suffered considerably in these circumstances. He
was unable to conceive of any other instinctual aim for himself; nevertheless, he felt this to be a failure in his masculine
development, all the more disturbing in that it involved a
number of character traits—sensibility to pain, submissiveness to
the point of cowardice, an uninspired pedantry, phlegm, and a
self-centeredness which notably hampered him. In addition, he
had strict religious scruples.

Family History

The father was a middle-grade official. According to the
patient, he was an adequate head of the household but not a
"real" father, of no help to his son in the difficulties of his
development. He was a "solipsist," a pedant and a prude. But,
underneath his phlegm, there was a suppressed vitality which
was discharged in quarrels with the patient's sister. His phlegm
was only a secondary trait, imposed by his upbringing or by
the patient's mother. He displayed a manliness which was alien
to him and a travesty but which nevertheless imposed itself as
an ideal which was not to be evaded.

His mother was gentle, sensitive, lacking in vitality, a "virgin-like" creature. Her girlishness was a defect but it was also her special attraction: "Under the naval she was made of celluloid." In spite of her patience, submissiveness and passivity, she was absolutely unyielding on matters of principles, particularly in the moral sphere, and she rigorously applied these principles in bringing up her children. She suffered because she was unable to make any compromise with herself. She lived in accordance with the principle: "Blessed are the meek."

The patient's sister was six years older than he. She was temperamental, wild, a "bohemian" type. She was her father's favorite, in spite of their quarrels under which the patient suffered throughout his childhood.

The fifth member of the household was the patient's maternal grandmother. She was emotionally uninhibited, simple, genuine, sensitive and religious. Her death, before he reached puberty, left an unfillable gap. The patient emphasized the predominant role played by women in his childhood.

II. SUMMARY OF THE ANALYSIS

Sessions 1–75

A large part of the patient's initial efforts was devoted to making clear to the analyst how his childhood situation had forced him into a permanent position of neutrality, passivity and control of all expression of feeling. He lived in perpetual secret opposition to his home climate, never daring to rebel openly. This went on until his schooldays, when he found an outlet in the society of his contemporaries. He was never really one of them, however, but led a life of his own. He managed to assume leading roles, as when he founded and inspired a theatrical group or assumed the role of "group conscience" for a number of boys.

After a more detailed description of his difficulties and peculiarities in relation to women, he remembered, to the accompaniment of great resistance and discomfort, that his interest in the color red and in beating had already awakened by the age of six or seven; he practiced the beating occasionally on his sister and, subsequently, on his schoolfellows; the feeling that he was doing something forbidden soon attached itself to this activity. In association with the resurrection of this long-forgotten memory, he produced a series of dreams in which, to his astonishment, he appeared as a woman. In one of them, for instance, he was a wife waiting for her husband and feeling oppressed because she knew herself to be impotent. In the subsequent sex act, in which he played the woman's role completely, he was indeed impotent.

He now proceeded to occupy himself with his female wish-picture. This was the masculine Amazon type which he sought out for his beating acts. He dreamed that a number of girls had to climb a spiral staircase, and that a powerful jet of water was directed at their buttocks as a substitute for the sex act; the jet was also directed at his own buttocks, and he felt himself to be one of the girls. He compared this female type with his mother, and stated that he had never had the feeling that she was a woman.

The patient's striving for "neutrality" and for a "functional, not a personal life" was distinctly expressed in this long first phase of the analysis, as well as in the transference. He repeatedly assured the analyst that he (the analyst) meant no more to him than a "blank wall," or, at most, "a kind of catalytic agent." On the other hand, in his transference he had enormous expectations of the analyst; he dreamed of him as a priest and as the practitioner of a religious-ritualistic kind of treatment which brought about a profound transformation in the patient.

Sessions 76–105

After the first fifty sessions, the patient became more and more aware of the extent to which he was bound to his mother, felt allied to her against his father, and claimed her for himself. He had phantasies about his mother and himself, both involved in secret guilt, standing in front of his father who threatened him with his fist; these phantasies, both in and out of analysis, resulted in tachycardia, diarrhoea, perspiration and attacks of anxiety. He sought in vain to check these effects by trying, in phantasy, to put his sister in his mother's place. Then the Oedipus legend occurred to this well-educated man, whose wide reading had not, however, included analytic literature. His response to this was a dream that his sister had married and that he had thereby become superfluous. Then there occurred a strong outburst of hatred against his mother; he stormed about her strait-laced adherence to principle, particularly in matters of punishment, her "subordinate" character, and her rejection—as if it were equivalent to libertinism—of everything that was not petty.

In this same phase of the analysis, the patient described how he had undergone a profound transformation between his eighth and fourteenth years; instead of his previous anxious defensive attitude toward school, he had transferred the true center of his life to the latter, and thus withdrawn himself from his home climate. In describing the home, he increasingly emphasized that his mother had not been able to counter the "powder-barrel" atmosphere created by the quarrels between his father and sister by the creation of a warm, loving atmosphere.

For the first time in the analysis, the patient experienced violent resistance; after this was overcome, there was an outburst of strong aggressive feelings in general and an interest in

beating in particular. He dreamed of wishing to violate his
sister and, soon afterwards, of beating his mother. Beating and
aggression seemed to him an assurance of manly superiority, a
counterweight to his passivity and attitude of surrender. He said
that he had associated pleasure feelings with beating from time
immemorial; his sexual excitements had always been coupled
with it. He had had sexual phantasies associated with beating
on the occasion of the first erection which he could remember,
at the age of about nine. He had always been so uncertain of his
virility that it was only with the aid of the feeling of superiority
induced by beating that he was able to confront the female
sex without losing confidence entirely.

The patient was sufficiently advanced analytically to desire
not merely to repress his perversion but to become free of it
at a deeper level. He even went through the beating procedure
with his woman friend in a more severe manner than ever before in the hope of a final break-through. In doing so, he experienced an erection, but without ejaculation, and was subsequently full of contrition. In the course of working through
this experience, memories of his mother's underclothes and
black stockings occurred to him; also, how he had sometimes
surprised her in the toilet. But he was more occupied with his
guilt feelings, with the sense of how artificial and legalistic his
religion was, and how strongly it was influenced by his mother.

Sessions 106–180

In this phase, the patient occupied himself particularly with
his feminine identification and came upon the problem of
masochism in himself. A strong tendency to get to grips positively with the masculine world manifested itself. The figures
of persons who had previously been in a position of authority
over him and had been criticized by him in an exclusively
negative way now appeared, first in his dreams and subsequently

in his associations, in a more positive light. His attitude to his father remained critical but the affective tone was no longer blindly negative; instead, he made efforts to understand his father's character. He would say, for instance, "He was no tyrant but I felt him to be so."

The patient also began developing insight into his excessive dependence on his mother and his feminine environment in general. He produced a series of dreams and associations bearing on his feminine identification. He remembered woolen garments belonging to his mother in which he nestled—her woolen bed-cover, her fur, into which he crept; and he recalled the pleasure with which he felt this world to be his own. He wanted to dress as a girl himself and played with the idea of buying himself a red jersey like those which had to be worn by the women whom he beat. He dreamed of himself as a girl and, in phantasy, had relations with his sister in which she was the man and he the girl. He spoke of his liking for seeing women in trousers; the reason for this, he thought, was that their doing so fulfilled to a large extent his wish to eliminate the polarity between the sexes. In other words, since he felt like a woman, he wanted to make the difference between himself and the female sex as imperceptible as possible.

When he came to recognize his excessive dependence on his mother and his deficient capacity to develop his own character, he dreamed of burning his mother's clothing and, perhaps, the mother herself. His pleasure in beating increased. He dreamed of beating his mother and was surprised by an interpretative idea that arose in his mind about this dream. "I beat her in protest against my own choice," he said. A completely new beating phantasy then arose: he was beating two women simultaneously; they were mother and daughter. His first association was that they were his women friend and her daughter; the next that they were his mother and himself. At the next session, it struck him for the first time that the object of his beating was, above all, himself. An earlier dream recurred to his mind in which he "and the other girls," as he put it, had a powerful jet of water directed at their buttocks. At the same session, it also struck him that the reason he had objected so strongly to wearing a jersey was that the latter was a fetish used to conceal a deeper wish in himself. The fact that, in his beating scenes, he wanted the woman to be dressed in a kind of athletic outfit, with tight brassière and knickers, was interpreted by him as follows: "Her clothes, though they bring out her shape, must not be typically feminine but almost like a uniform or, at any rate, athletic. I must know that she is a woman but I do not use her as a woman. She must be exchangeable with myself. I am not interested in her genital zone. All I want is the beating itself."

Next night, he dreamed of his mother, wearing a tight corset, in the role of a female sadist, leaning on a riding-whip. He had the sudden feeling, accompanied by severe anxiety and tachycardia, that his whole previous conception of his perversion was suddenly being reversed, that the beating was directed against himself and that, at the core of his sadism, masochism lay concealed.

The feeling of complete dependence on his mother, in which he lived and which made him seek to resemble her, seized him to the accompaniment of great anxiety. Feelings of his own nothingness and memories of self-punishment tendencies in his childhood overwhelmed him. He remembered, for instance, putting a pea in his shoe and keeping it there for days after telling a lie, as well as committing other acts of self-castration. He started out of a dream in which he was asked his name, and caught himself calling out the name of the girl on whom he had carried out his beating act for the first time and with whom—incidentally, in a situation of great danger, in which death seemed near—he had succeeded for the first time in his life in having coitus, though with premature ejaculation.

From this session onward, the analysis was dominated for a long time by the patient's mother in the role of sadist, wearing a black dress buttoned to the top and standing in the alcove in which he beat his sister.

With this elucidation of the patient's relationship of dependence on his mother, I believe that a decisive approach to the root-problem of his sado-masochistic perversion was made.

Sessions 181–240

In this phase the patient occupied himself predominantly with the problem of his homo-eroticism; it became plain to him that this was an inadequate refuge from the genital-sexual position.

Already during the previous phase, the patient had adhered to an active, exclusively male, debating club, and his membership became one of his most powerful resistances. It took him a long time to realize that the extraordinary amount of satisfaction he derived from his club was a psychodynamic factor of the first importance which had to be worked through analytically. He insisted on the necessity of living fully through the male relationships involved even if, for the time, it removed him further from his real desire, which was to be able to attain a satisfactory relationship with a woman. He managed, within a very short time, to play an important role in his party. The release of his aggression through the analysis enabled him to become a sought-after debater and his intellectual gifts enabled him to master the most difficult material. He acquired a number of younger and older friends, to whom he became bound by a strong emotional tie which he found pleasurable and consciously enjoyed.

However, the greater his external successes, the more questionable they became. The success that he earned as a public speaker turned to ashes because he noticed that, though he could generally win a debate, he failed to appeal to the hearts of his audience. "They feel that I don't love them, but only use them as a tool," he said. A sermon on the text: "Peter, dost thou love me?" struck him like a hammer-blow. He associated the analyst with this, and had an entirely new feeling toward him: profound sympathy, because he constantly made superhuman demands on him and at the same time wished to use him only as a "tool." The "white wall" picture he had applied to the analyst recurred to him, to the accompaniment of deep guilt. When he confessed this, he blushed deeply and, at the same time, defended himself against a wave of affection for the analyst.

He began to be greatly occupied with his relations with his father. On the one hand, he started recognizing the extent to which he projected father-figures on to the older club members. Finally, he succeeded in coming into a closer and more balanced relationship with his strongest rival, based on mutual respect and a certain amount of liking. He now built himself a single father-imago based on the pattern of this older man which, because of the "removal" of ambivalence, was very close to life. Working through his relationship with this man contributed a great deal to his progress toward maturity.

In his relations with this father-figure in his actual environment he worked through in many respects the picture he had formed of his real father and his relations with the latter. He learned to accept his father's failure as a human tragedy.

The patient's emotional link with one of his friends became

so strong that its homo-erotic component became plain to him. He discovered the same element in numerous relationships he had had with men, even including the men who persecuted him during his time in a P.O.W. camp. This made him feel the immaturity of his human contacts—he had never had a real relationship even with his enemies.

Henceforward, his interest in beating appeared to him in a new light; he regarded it as a love-test, a means of testing the solidity of a relationship. His memories and phantasies reverted more and more to his fourth year. He had phantasies of running to his mother and striking her. She understood this, not as an appeal but as an attack on her authority (which she used to punish him and push him back into the child's "functional" position). Or he saw his father coming in and angrily rebuking him for striking his mother. This now appeared to him a perverted sex act.

Another aspect of his father was revealed in this phase of the analysis: the forbidding authoritarian who had intercourse with his mother while the patient had phantasies of being in bed beside them. Castration fears played an increasing role. He felt himself to be falling into a deep black pit; his member was nipped off upon entry; he was crushed in the vagina of a big woman who belonged to his father. A rescuing figure appeared from time to time in these phantasies and dreams—that of his grandmother with whom, as a child, he had had his happiest emotional relationship.

Along with the appearance of castration fears, a number of other memories, connected with the anal sphere, were produced. These, both with reference to his own anal region and, in particular, the female anal region, were experienced with intense pleasure. In describing these anal associations and memories, the castration fears faded away but the beating phantasies increased again and, with them, the patient's pre-occupation with the fragility of his human relations. Homo-eroticism now seemed to him more and more an unsatisfactory and dishonest evasion.

Sessions 241-310

In the next phase of the analysis, the patient got to grips with the necessity of attaining genital-sexual maturity. The transference came increasingly into the foreground. To the accompaniment of strong aggressive feelings, the patient faced the problem of his relations with the analyst who, he felt, was driving him into a disastrous situation by disturbing his present idyll with his woman friend. The patient became increasingly aware of the extent to which he had transferred to the analyst his Oedipal hatred of his father, against whose sexual taboos he raged. Not having revolted in his youth, he revolted now and, as his home standards and taboos derived principally from his mother, his strongest aggression was directed against her. He dreamed of murdering her and, with her, God and the analyst, all of whom belonged together. It was they who, both in the past and the present, repressed his wishes and directed him toward objective norms—rightly, he had to admit. The patient found himself increasingly opposed to the rigidly orthodox religious views he had previously held but which he now felt to be negative and hostile to life.

The figure of his sister temporarily occupied a key position in the analysis. In dreams and phantasies, he beat her; scenes from his early childhood, in which he found pleasure in beating her buttocks, recurred. At the same time, he became aware of a fondness for her which he had previously concealed. His beating her now seemed to be a love-test, in the sense that he could not confidently rely on being loved simply as he was.

He thought that he carried out the love-test on the buttocks because he had withdrawn from the genital sphere, because of the paternal taboos, and because he had had, or at any rate thought that he had had, the closest physical relations with his mother in the beating act.

While his sister thus came into the foreground in his aggressive phantasies, there took place an eruption of pregenital material associated with his mother. This was introduced by a dream of red stains on the patient's nightshirt, in which he thought he recognized his own menstrual blood. He associated with this the ambivalent attitude he had always had toward wool and cotton-wool, as well as toward the phenomenon of menstruation. The thought of the latter had always been unpleasant to him and linked with the idea of castration. He now increasingly associated the idea of the red jersey with it and with his mother's bare body, seeing which in his childhood meant punishment. In this context, beating seemed to him to be a punishment incurred for transgression of this taboo; as a way of fighting this idea, he passed on the punishment to the woman wearing the red jersey.

Simultaneously, phantasies of fellatio appeared for the first time. These were more and more definitely directed toward his mother and, in association with them, the patient vainly sought to imagine his mother in the red jersey. Then there was a kaleidoscopic rush of phantasies. The red jersey appeared as a phallus; the figure of his mother as "a big woman with phallus attached" (in the form of the red jersey) arose and overwhelmed him with severe feelings of aggression and anxiety.

He freed himself from the picture of the phallic mother by recognizing the phallus as his own; the way toward this critical solution had already been prepared and indicated in a wider framework. In the massive liberations of aggression—

which, from the point of view of resistance, were made substantially easier by their displacement on to his sister—there
grew in the patient the feeling of "greater personal weight."
He discovered as something entirely new in himself that he no
longer had inhibitions about identifying himself with himself,
but could now say, "Yes, that is me." He was now able to integrate the phallic into the new awareness of his own personality. The red jersey lost its phallic aspect and was now
felt as a protective covering, the female genitals. The idea
that he might achieve normal relations with a woman was
now pleasurably cathected.

Abiding in the maternal world no longer meant security for
him, but bondage.

Sessions 311–345

A few weeks later, the patient made the acquaintance of
a woman five years younger than himself toward whom he
quickly developed a lively inclination. "For the first time, I
felt with a woman that I was not falling into a bottomless pit
—and I also felt tenderness without aggression." The night
after the first exchanges of tenderness took place, the patient
was overcome with deep feelings of guilt. The feeling that he
was letting his mother down led him for days into excessive
masturbation. But then his tender feelings once more concentrated entirely on the woman and he felt the awakening
of a masculine demand in himself. He became aware of a
new kind of aggression—the "expression of a feeling of tenderness which, being overfull, seeks discharge." He dreamed that
he had a very big member and discovered that for the first
time, he was taking pleasure in his sex. The fact that he was
still impotent in intercourse pained but did not discourage
him. He felt certain that, within a foreseeable period, coitus

with this woman would be possible because in relation to her the impulse did not come from any kind of external circumstance. She was the only person with whom he had had a personal relationship for a long time—"simply because she is, not because she is a function." His association with her gave him a blissful feeling of acceptance of his own body which now became much more important to him. He found his impotence increasingly irritating, no longer for the reasons of "principle" which he had alleged at the beginning of the analysis, but because it hurt him—for the woman's sake as well—not to be able "to co-ordinate his general feelings with proper physical contact."

Beating and anal phantasies once more came into the foreground and he connected them more and more closely. Hitherto, he had always been uninterested in the genital zone but had taken all the more interest in the anal zone; he said that the object of his beating a woman was to involve his own anal zone in the experience. He increasingly discovered "tenderness in the form of aggression" behind the beating, and the more physical contact and happiness he enjoyed with his new woman friend, the more there arose in his mind pleasurable memories and phantasies having an anal content. In being touched, he thought that he detected physical care; he said that touching the anal zone represented the most intimate conceivable contact with the being he loved. He remembered the pleasurable interest he had taken, in infancy, in the act of defecation and his pride in its completion. He recalled the pleasurable feelings associated with his mother's giving him an enema.

But here, too, he felt himself frustrated by his mother. She had been clumsy in the application of the enema and very impatient with his interest in its products. In a phantasy that occupied him for weeks—he was unable positively to differentiate it from a memory—he thought he had found the key to his ambivalent and, above all, fear-tinged attitude to women; his mother had refused to accept his feces and made him get rid of them in the lavatory. He thought of this as having occurred at an age when he must still have been wearing a dress. Thus his mother had rejected him as a love-partner when his emotions were still in the anal stage.

On the one hand, he now felt his beating to be an unleashing of aggression in response to female rejection of his feelings; on the other, he felt that it was really he who was being beaten and that he took pleasure in it because of his concentration upon anal feelings. Thus the simultaneously sadistic and maso-chist components of beating emerged plainly as directed against himself.

Phantasies increasingly arose of sexual intercourse between his parents in which his father humiliated his mother, robbed her of her noble pose and forced her to experience the life of the senses. At the same time, hate-feelings toward his father ap-peared once more. In phantasies and dreams he desired his father's death. "Father takes his life, and now *I* am the man."

Sessions 346–400

This last phase was decisively influenced by external circum-stances which brought the analysis to an end. During its course, the patient's capacities developed in an extraordinary fashion; he gained rapid promotion and was transferred abroad. He therefore broke off his analysis, confident that he had set foot on a path which would enable him to complete the last lap alone. He also took another important decision: to marry before his departure.

He had not yet reached full potency but believed himself to be well on the road to it. He had completely lost his tendencies to fetishism and his sado-masochistic inclinations had nearly disappeared; they now occupied him only in occasional phantasies, particularly in relation to his mother. But he no longer felt the urge to carry them out, particularly not upon his woman friend. Pleasurable ideas of normal relations with her moved into the foreground, accompanied by increasingly stronger erections. Eventually, he succeeded in achieving penetration pleasurably and without anxiety, though he still failed to achieve orgasm, except for an occasional premature ejaculation.

He was much occupied, in this phase of the analysis, with his father's inadequacy as a father-figure, and the question whether he had not made excessive demands on him and done too little himself to go forward to meet him. He did not directly connect his guilt feelings about this with castration fears directed toward his father and deriving from the Oedipal phase; the guilt feelings led him back to the identification with his mother and to castration fears and wishes associated with her. "I wish to get rid of my member because mother has not got one." He dreamed of having breasts and a small penis between them. In his associations, he had phantasies of fellatio as an escape from castration. He saw in this the wish of a boy who knows nothing but being with his mother. He had phantasies of a suckling being quieted and produced memories of clinging to his mother's hair and her fur; and he associated the red jersey with his grandmother's shawl and the shawls in which a baby is wrapped. He saw his beating impulse in a new light: as being both an expression of aggression because of tenderness not granted him and an act of revenge because the identification he felt to be imposed on him permitted him no independence. "I want to be loved by the woman. I beat her—because I do not wish to deliver myself up to her—not so severely as to destroy her love but severely enough to put a strain on it. The tie must be stretched, but not broken."

These pregenital themes were followed by phantasies of parental coitus, with which beating was connected as a punishment inflicted on his mother for an action incompatible with her lofty moral attitude, an action, moreover, which she forbade the patient. He also felt that the beating symbolized coitus as a process in which his father made his otherwise so prudish mother submit to him. On the one hand, his mother's humiliation gave him deep satisfaction and, on the other, it filled him with jealousy of his father. He imagined scenes on the red sofa in the sitting room in his home in which his father had relations with his mother to the accompaniment of much flagellation. Then he busied himself with ideas that his beating was a perverted sex act and that he was introducing his member as a sword with sadistic pleasure in hurting his mother. He responded to these phantasies with ideas of castration and punishment, in which he felt incomparably less threatened by his father than by his mother. But these anxiety-filled phantasies faded away again and, simultaneously, he felt a strengthening of his genital desires for his woman friend.

In the last hours of the analysis, the patient saw his difficulties in relation to his father as being based on secret guilt at his inability to step out of the feminine sphere, identification with his mother. It was this which, in his childhood, had made him feel that his father was continually admonishing him to develop his masculinity, and that he himself had therefore taken the wrong path. Whenever he had tried to enter into a relationship with his father, he had immediately made an exaggerated attempt to make himself equivalent to him. "That was my earlier guilty error; that, in my stubbornness, I did not consent to being merely a child, the child of my mother and father.

I had the hybrid feeling that, in emotional relationships, I must be the same as he. Hence my perfectionism and freedom in love were abolished. The same thing entered into my relationship with God. I could conceive of it only as a reactive relationship, not as a free relationship in which the next meeting with God is not to be foreseen. That made me feel all the more abandoned."

He could talk like this now because, in his relations with his woman friend, it had become plain to him that, in love, anxiety about "equality of rights" is without foundation. From this, he went on to a deep serenity: "I now want a relationship of communication, not of identification," he said. He withdrew to a large extent from his excessive club activity, which he now recognized as having been "a huge retreat from his own life," and found time for quiet evenings, in which he devoted himself to his own soul, as he put it. He found his way back to a real religious life, without the perfectionism and the rigid codes which had previously made religion so emotionally meaningless.

At this stage, the analysis was broken off.

III. EPICRITICAL REMARKS

In his paper, *A Child Is Being Beaten*, Freud maintains that beating phantasies in the male sex are based upon the inverted Oedipus complex taking the father as the love object. In his elaboration of the beating phantasies, the boy substitutes the mother for the father but keeps his own identity, "with the result that the person beating and the person being beaten are of opposite sexes. . . . In the case of the boy, the situation remains masochistic, and shows a greater resemblance to the original phantasy with its genital significance, since there is a difference of sex between the person beating and the person being beaten. The boy evades his homosexuality by repressing and remodeling his unconscious phantasy."[1]

My case differs from Freud's observations in some essential points. Instead of being feminine and masochistic, the conscious phantasies of the patient show a sadistic pattern. On the other hand, he experiences himself in his dreams in a feminine sexual position. It is not a boy who is beaten in his phantasies but a girl; the beating person is either he himself or a female person of authority.

Freud derives the beating phantasy from the incestuous ties to the father. The incestuous links of my patient, however, were directed toward the mother, and that not because of a predominant Oedipus complex, e.g., a regressive identification with the mother in order to escape the castration threat from the father. There were some such fears emerging in the analysis but they played a subordinate role only. In my case, the decisive factor seems rather to be the pregenital fixation upon the mother. The patient entered the Oedipal stage in tense dependence from the maternal world. This dependence was strengthened by the fact that the father failed to a large extent, to stand for a positive formative figure and that the female element was preponderant in the patient's environment.

Thus, upon entering the Oedipal phase, it was the mother who became the identification figure for the patient. The castration fears were to a large extent ascribed to the mother rather than to the father. Because of his identification with her, he was not allowed to become a man. He still lived in a "pseudo-separation of the Ego and the You," "on a phantasy level determined by the still unbroken unity of world and Ego or, more exactly, the You and the Ego." He remained "in a retarded separation of the primary love reality of the You and the Ego."[2] His fetishistic tendencies did not so much correspond to a genital-sexual pattern as to a pregenital pattern. It is true that the phallic mother appeared in the analysis; the boy had lent her what he in reality observed in himself and what she, the primary identification figure, must possess unless the likeness was disturbed. As the patient acquired sufficient personal substantiality to accept the phallic aspect of the red jersey as a "fetish," and to withdraw this aspect from the mother on to himself, its feminine aspect made a fleeting appearance in the image of the female genitals changing into images of sheltering covers like diapers or his grandmother's shawl. Not the genital but rather the pregenital reality seems decisive.

An essential condition for his seeking to find his love reality in sadistic beating was the personality structure of his own mother, along with the fact that, in the pregenital phase, he was still unhindered to live out his libido but failed in the identification requirements of the Oedipal phase. Beating for him had a complex meaning; the analysis revealed how its aspects changed in the course of his biographic development, and how each phase added to the existing stock of meanings. Beating had not only sadistic but also masochistic aspects, inasmuch as, in it, he saw himself as the beaten child; the phantasy was not projected on to a boy because of his still feminine identification. Here again the pregenital factor seems essential: "the links are only stretched, not broken"—i.e., the primary separation was not yet achieved.

The results of this analysis do not contradict in principle the conceptions of Freud; it is possible that they add to them. Although I do not, in any way, intend to underestimate the pathoplastic strength of the Oedipal situation—over and above the father problem and homo-erotic tendencies this became evident in the patient's religious struggles—nevertheless, this case and its pathogenesis call for the consideration of the pregenital problems.

REFERENCES

1 Freud, Sigmund. "A Child Is Being Beaten" (1919). *Coll. Papers,* Vol. II. London, 1924.

2 Gebsattel, V. E., Frhr. v. "Über fetischismus." *Nervenarzt,* Vol. II, 1929.

Aggression and Perversion

ROBERT C. BAK

Perversions generally imply the dominance of pregenitality in the sexual function. This regressive feature is common to all perversions and involves the denial of heightened castration anxiety and marked bisexual identification. The ambivalent cathexis of the object with preponderance of destructiveness is a corollary in the pregenital stages. The role of sadism in the formation of perversions has lately been more and more emphasized by several authors (Klein, Glover, Payne, Gillespie, Greenacre) and we may add that the emphasis in our etiological thinking has shifted from the traumata of the phallic phase to the traumatic influences of the pre-phallic era. This shift has taken place—though by no means in explicit connection—simultaneously with our greater attention to the role of aggression in mental functioning and in pathology as well.

In attempting to highlight the role of aggression in sexual deviations, obvious repetitions of previously known facts, as well as a certain one-sidedness, seem hardly avoidable. But it does not mean in any sense a disregard of the various vicissitudes of libido.

Psychoanalytic etiology rests on the concept of fixation. In fixation, the quantitative factor of "arrest" was later complemented by the functional aspect (emphimixis—Ferenczi), and finally the temporal factor gained in significance. Our concepts of fixation were developed almost entirely in relation to libidinal development. Their causation, besides the constitutional factor, was regarded as the consequence either of overindulgence or of deprivation. The question of constitutional predisposition, where elements of the sexual drive are concerned, has been present in psychoanalysis from its beginnings. We still think in terms of the complementary series (Freud, Sadger, Abraham), even though its importance in pathogenesis has been lessened with the introduction of the temporal factor. Also, the extreme pliability of the sexual drive as to its object, which is the least constant factor, should caution us in assuming a constitutional factor concerning a particular element of the sexual drive. Freud's last statement about constitutional predisposition referred to a possible variation in the distribution of the two basic drives and hinted at the possible role that aggression may play in psychic conflict in general. Though there is no way of proving it, we assume, in perversions, an increased quantity of aggression either constitutionally or, as we will see later, as the consequence of those very early environmental stresses that sometimes increase the impetus of the aggressive drive.

The complexity of situations in evaluating the developmental influences increases once one considers the vicissitudes of aggression at the same time. It seems almost needless to emphasize that environmental influences are more or less apt to produce reactions in either drive. The ensuing reactions will depend on the temporal factor and especially on the *stage of structural development* and on *the established grade of object relationship*. The stage of object relationship, probably, is of particular importance, and it may well be that the group of perversions that are ego-syntonic—and so, for the most part, escape our investigation—contain highly developed object relationships and originate from the phase near the Oedipus constellation.

Clinical experience indicates that, in cases of multiple perversions, traumatic overstimulation occurred in the undifferentiated phase, thereby affecting both drives in their undifferentiated state simultaneously. Physiological dysfunctions threatening survival, and the disequilibrium of mother-child relationship (Greenacre) in this early phase, seemed to be present in several cases of perversion. Its sensory consequences, forming identification, were also described by Greenacre in rich detail in relation to fetishism. One may surmise, however, that at least some of these findings cannot be restricted as the determinant of fetishism only, especially since we rarely encounter perversions in isolation. Whereas, in fetishism, the uncertainty of body image and especially the confused sexual identity may be most striking, the vagueness of body periphery, of the boundaries of the body-self, may well be a substratum of all perversions. It certainly plays a much greater role in sado-masochism than has hitherto been emphasized. The overstimulation of undifferentiated libido and aggression may be one determinant for the heightened sadistic disposition with its character of unusual inner pressure and driven-ness for gratification. Large quantities of excitation, at a time when ego development is at its beginning, may establish the tendency to uncontrolled libidinal and aggressive discharge without interference from the ego. Defenses at this stage are necessarily autoplastic and largely based on magic omnipotence—which consists mainly of a denial of the outside world. *Denials in later stages may well draw from this early-established magic pattern.* Among the defensive measures, the main role seems to be played by "overflowing" between self and object which, in the progress of ego development, may give way to processes of primary identification and the introjection-projection mechanisms emphasized by the British school. Perversions in which the above-described genetic history is discernible show a clinical closeness to schizophrenia, or else the patients have schizophrenic symptoms at the same time. In such cases, it is almost impossible to make a clear distinction between the schizophrenic identification and defenses and those underlying the perversion. Their frequent co-existence shows the fluidity of these mechanisms in one individual. One may say that, in the schizophrenic symptoms, the regression to undifferentiation has taken place and that the partial narcissistic object relationships in the perverse symptoms are reparative attempts. *They seem to represent different forms of defense against the unneutralized aggression threatening the object.* It is not too unlikely to assume that, in schizophrenic manifestations, due to the undifferentiation of both bad and good objects and libido and aggression, a more extensive withdrawal from the object world takes place than in perversions where, by splitting of the self, a narcissistic object relation can be maintained. It seems likely that overstimulation in the undifferentiated phase especially damages the neutralization function of the ego but it is also possible that discharge patterns are established and regressed to when neutralization has not yet begun. Clinically, this is most relevant to those schizophrenia-near perversions in which libido and aggression retain a large quantity of the undifferentiation and where the bad object is retained in introjected and projected forms. But it is also relevant to perversions where a more differentiated object relationship exists. The disturbance in object relationship—specifically, genital object love—is evident in all perversions; genital object love itself is dependent on a high degree of neutralization. Therefore, it would seem preferable to think in terms of differentiation of the two drives rather than their "fusion" in genitality (the more so if we accept a definition of sadism as the fusion of the two drives). It seems that it is exactly one of the ego's major functions to differentiate the two drives and specialize their aims. The ego's ability to neutralize aggression is one of the major mechanisms hitherto described in the service of this larger ego function of differentiating, deflecting large quantities of aggression from sexuality. A certain interdependence between object relation, repression and neutralization has been previously stated. In perversions, instead of a maturationally progressing neutralization, the ego defends itself and the object by identification and a partial projection of the self in establishing narcissistic object relationships. It has been emphasized that the formation of the Oedipus constellation itself depends on the pregenital history. In pregenital fixations, we emphasize primarily the quantity and object of unneutralized aggression. If, from one or several pregenital sources, the phallic phase is weakened by the quantity of destructive impulses toward the love object, the consequence is not only the threat to the object; the passive libidinal aims remain directed toward the object of the same sex. Among the reasons for a predominantly negative Oedipus, we point out again the earlier identification with the object that occurred as a defense against destruction due, on the one hand, to disturbed neutralization, on the other, to the importance of the love object. This lack of specialization in the object of the two drives may even prevent the development of an Oedipus phase and especially of a positive one.

The Oedipus phase and its resolution, under ideal circumstances, prepares the setting by which at the time of genital maturation, the two basic drives reach: (1) optimal differentiation; (2) integration of the sexual drive in genital primacy. Since integration of the final aim of aggression cannot be reached in human development (3) neutralization of residual aggression in ego function and superego formation has to take place instead of a reflex inhibition against killing the same species (Lorenz). Finally, specialization of the two drives by which the sexual drive is directed toward an object of the different sex, retaining an adequate quantity of aggression for purposeful action, whereas the aggressive drive is directed toward objects of the same sex, enabling rivalry with enough libidinal quantity for social relationships.

Failure in any of these factors will eventually lead to pathology. In the group of perversions, in addition to repression and other defenses against the fixated drive representatives, regression takes place and *the ego undergoes a narcissistic split. One part of the self allies itself with either basic drive and this alliance, or syntonicity, will constitute the overt manifestations of the perversion.* The other part of the self, which is allied with the ego-alien drive, is relegated to the object. This process seems to be a regressive adaptation of the ego by the split between self and object and, at the same time, an attempt at the differentiation of the two drives. It is similar to, although not identical with, what Freud described in fetishism; the split does not concern contradictory, or rival, perceptual contents but is closer to denial which places the expelled "bad" drive "outside" the ego. This narcissistic split is present in scoptophilia, exhibitionism and sado-masochism *and* plays an important role in homosexuality (Anna Freud).

It is obvious that the exhibitionist reassures himself against castration. The acting out of this aggression is a denial of the deeper-lying feminine identification. The male exhibitionist is identified with the female child and maintains awe and aggressive ambivalence toward the paternal phallus. Due to the greater ego syntonicity of aggression in men, the passive-feminine self will be externalized to the object.

The fetishist escapes castration fear by the denial of his perception that women lack a penis. The denial is also necessitated by his alternating between identification with the phallic and aphallic mother. However, this description should be supplemented by what Payne, Gillespie and Greenacre have emphasized, that the fetish is revered as a denial and protection against the destructive wishes directed at the object, especially the breast (Gillespie). Further material on fetishists indicates a strong prohibition of oral-sadistic phantasies (biting of the nipple), defended not only by the fetish but, in one case, by alcoholic stupor serving as a defense against his devouring and realizing a state of oral bliss and identification with the love object. (Greenacre has already hinted at the connection between drug addiction and fetishism.) It seems that fixation in pregenital aggression is a genetic requirement for the appearance of the fetish in or after the phallic phase. The insistence on the female phallus represents a breast-penis identification and serves also as the denial of the destructive wishes against the breast. Hence the emphasis on the indestructible character of the fetish and the need for its presence. The fear of retaliation that threatens the fetishist comes more from the woman *because she remains predominantly the object of his aggression* and her aphallic state revives the phantasy of devouring the breast with the consequent fear of retaliation. The "independence" of the fetishist from the object, "the complete possession" of the symbolic substitute, indicates the gratification of aggression and of omnipotence. The denial of aggression in the libidinized reverence of the substitute or partial object both prevents castration and saves the object from destruction. In fetishism, the ego attempts an integration of both drives but, due to the predominance of destructiveness, it can direct it *only at the symbolic substitute*. In a fetishist, the fetish in the object choice becomes less pronounced when sexual functioning is less guilt-ridden by sadistic phantasies during sexual activity.

Transvestism has basic mechanisms in common with fetishism though the relationship to total object is more prevailing than in the fetishist. The transvestite defends himself against the loss of the object by taking on its external appearance. This defense accomplishes the denial of castration and of the disappearance—considered as destruction by the id—of the object.

In connection with the complex problem of homosexuality, we refer here to the four mechanisms described by Freud:

1. Narcissism.

2. The intense attachment to the mother that led to identification.

3. The castration complex, with its narcissistic over-valuation of the penis resulting in "penis awe" (Greenacre).

4. The shifting from aggressive rivalry to love by making the object of aggression into the object of sexuality.

Today the role of aggression is evident for us even in the first three mechanisms that are not obviously vicissitudes of aggression.

I have emphasized, in the foregoing, the function of narcissism in binding aggressive energies and the role that aggression plays in identification. It is almost needless to add that the "intense attachment" to the mother, which led to identification with her, contains an intermediate phase of aggression motivated by disappointment. As to the intensity of the castration complex, I have emphasized the passive libidinal attitude toward the father as a consequence of unneutralized aggression against the mother and its interwovenness with bisexual identification.*

* Freud (Hemmung) in connection with "Little Hans"—sadistic aggression, masochistic love (a pair of opposites) both implying castration danger.

Finally, in taking the rival as the love object—a mechanism more general in homosexuality than hitherto claimed.

Homosexuals show a failure in all four factors that are necessary for the resolution of the Oedipus complex. In turning away from heterosexual objects by identification, the destructive impulses against the mother are resolved and, at the same time, they pave the way for libidinization of aggression against the rival. The homosexual thus succeeds in defending himself against retaliation from both sexes. There are manifold variations in the compromise between aggression and libido (Nunberg) and whether, through narcissistic split, aggressive or libidinal attitudes are delegated to the object (also Anna Freud). In addition, elements which we mentioned in connection with other perversions are present to a greater or lesser extent, just as all other perversions show a degree of homosexuality due to their ubiquitous narcissistic elements and bisexual identification.

Summary

1. This paper attempts to integrate aggression into sexual pathology as an "equal partner" of libido.

2. Perversions are considered as symptoms in which the dominant defense—*common to all perversions—is the dramatized denial of castration* and in which the gratification of libido consists of a genetically-determined variety of pregenital fixations.

3. The increased need to deny castration is based, on the one hand, upon the projection of a heightened aggression, on the other, on a marked bisexual identification, which was established as a defense against the destruction of the object, in whole or in part.

4. *The increased impetus* of the aggressive drive is regarded

as the consequence of overstimulation in the undifferentiated phase. This may result (outside constitutional factors) either in *damage* to the neutralization function of the ego, caused by the overexcitation or to the establishment of *discharge patterns* prior to ego development.

5. The frequent coexistence of schizophrenic symptoms with perversions indicates a common fixation point in the undifferentiated phase and in defenses against unneutralized aggression; the perverse symptoms represent an attempt at restitution of the narcissistic object relationship.

6. Common to all perversions is the narcissistic object relationship established by the *splitting of the self*. The distance from schizophrenia depends on the *grade of structural development* and the *grade of object relationship*.

7. Since object relationship depends on neutralization, one may assume the failure of this ego function in all perversions.

8. It is further hypothesized that *it is a task of the ego to differentiate the two drives as to their aim and object*. Neutralization tends toward changes of the aim, whereas the differentiation as to the object of the drive fails in perversions; i.e., the love object remains the object of aggression.

9. In conclusion: perverse symptoms are regressive adaptations of the ego to secure sexual gratification without destroying the object and endangering the self which is identified with the object.

IV

Other Forms of
Perversions

Male Genital Exhibitionism

HANS CHRISTOFFEL

The following pages contain a survey of the characteristics of male genital exhibitionism (MGE) from the point of view of the psychology of the individual and of social psychology. It has been compiled from hundreds of pages of notes based on the observation of eleven patients, as well as a large number of other cases.

Cultural Background

Exhibitionism is the first thing mentioned in the *Characters* of Theophrastus (about 370-287 B.C.) when he comes to deal with "grossness" or "buffoonery" (βδελυρίας). "The buffoon is one that will lift his shirt in the presence of free-born women," he writes, "and at the theatre will applaud when others cease, hiss actors whom the rest of the audience approves, and raise his head and hiccup when the house is silent. . . . He will call by name one of the company with whom he is not well acquainted . . . and when he would spit something out, he spits it across the table at the butler." People similar to this Athenian type of the fourth century B.C. exist in the conditions of contemporary Western Europe but, as I gather from J. E.

Staehelin,[16] and according to my own estimate, they constitute barely ten percent of the total number of MGE's. The historical background of the Chinese novel *Chin P'ing Mei* is provided by the years 1111-1127 A. D.[10] It contains an account of how seven or eight maids and servants' wives attack a young man who had caused their mistress displeasure. They "surrounded him, and began to belabor him furiously with short cudgels and with long. Taken by surprise, he already lay on the ground when a saving thought occurred to him in his distress; and, in an instant, he had divested himself of his trousers. Appalled by such a terrible sight, the women hastily dispersed." This ancient Chinese method of self-defense has an affinity with a specimen of Yugoslav behavior, reported by S. F. Krauss[13] at the turn of the century. If a man wishes to make a gesture of supreme contempt, Krauss says, he angrily exposes his genitals; alternatively, he may use sexually humiliating expletives. At the Basle municipal theatre in 1939, a nervous actor, about to make his début, had an erection which was easily perceptible through his trousers and caused laughter among the chorus. An experienced actor reported in connection with this incident that it was formerly a stage custom that the tenor, in particular, should have an erection before a first performance or, alternatively, should simulate one. The latter was achieved by the introduction into the trousers of a hare's foot ("hare's foot" was a device for removing grease paint and may, originally, have been really the foot of a hare). This "stage-fright" or "hare's-foot" variety of exhibitionism is thus the ritualization of personal readiness. There is, however, a relationship between this traditionally concealed genital exhibitionism and the exaggerated genital display in the armour of fifteenth and sixteenth century mercenaries—as we know it from the drawings of Urs Graf, etc. The phenomenon of *shook-yong*, or *koro*, can

be classified with these aggressive or defensive types of exhibitionism. In the land of Chin P'ing Mei, as elsewhere
in the Far East,[21] men succumb to attacks in which they
believe that their sexual organs are in danger of disappearing
into the interior of their bodies and killing them. I last heard
of this phenomenon in 1949. These attacks of *koro* are accompanied by terrible anxiety and vary in duration from a
few hours to a few days; they tend more or less to recur.
During the attack, the genital organs are held and tended by
males or females until the patient feels able to trust them
again. An isolated instance of a phobia of this kind was recently briefly reported from southwestern Germany, unfortunately without being investigated. It was that of a man of
twenty-nine who attached his member to the skin of his belly
with sticking-plaster. National or popular peculiarities of this
kind serve to put one on the alert for the phobic aspect of
MGE; the fear felt by the victim of *koro* in relation to his own
male body is, in MGE, directed toward the body of the opposite sex, the female sexual organ in particular.

Exhibitionism was introduced into psychopathology by the
Paris psychiatrist and neurologist, E. C. Lasègue's (1818-1863).
In Lasègue's mother-tongue, French, *exhibition* means a special
display within the framework of a general exhibition. "Exhibition" is, however, also a term in international law, meaning
"production" of a document—*exhibition d'un passeport,* for
example. The term "exhibition," in the sexual sense, made rapid
headway in medical literature but many years passed before it
gained admission to general reference books, such as the ency-
clopedias of Larousse or Brockhaus. The legal definition of *exhibition* did not recede into the background or disappear altogether until sixty or seventy years after the introduction of the
psychopathological concept of exhibitionism. Thus, in the lan-

guage of educated people, a transformation in the meaning of the term took place at about the turn of the century.

MGE is of sufficiently frequent occurrence in our civilization for Lasègue to have stated in 1877 that he had observed "many" instances. According to A. Kronfeld (1926), not a day passed without a case's being reported to the police; M. Hirschfeld, in Berlin in 1926, reported "several hundred" cases on his own authority; and B. Dukor, psychiatrist to the Basle court, has been kind enough to inform me that, according to official figures and estimates, there were 565 convictions in Switzerland for MGE in 1951 and 617 in 1952.

It is, therefore, all the more remarkable that MGE is not included in A. C. Kinsey's sexual statistics about more than 12,000 males in the United States (1948). Kinsey is aware only of the "genital exhibition of younger boys" and mentions exhibitionism only as "preadolescent sex play." That the absence from his statistics of a single case of MGE is the fault of Kinsey and his collaborators is suggested by the fact that in 1954, L. Eidelberg[5] not only gave an account of MGE in the United States but had obviously extended and deepened the knowledge of the subject he had previously acquired in Europe. The gap in the Kinsey report can be readily explained by the fact that the male genital exhibitionist is not an exhibitionist in every respect but is generally shy and shut up within himself.

Another remarkable fact is that, as Lasègue[20] points out, there seems to be no popular term for MGE. I have myself had Paris *argot* and French *patois* searched for such a term. But the result was as negative as was an examination of Swiss-German popular vocabularies.

O. Fenichel[6] describes MGE as an attempt to overcome anxiety "by the simple hypertrophy of an infantile component instinct," but that does not conceal the fact that the MGE syndrome as a whole is a complicated structure; a phobic-perverse syndrome, which has been in preparation since infancy, breaks out catastrophically in the early years of manhood, and may persist for months or decades. The phobic aspect of MGE consists principally of kolpophobias and claustrophobias; marital conditions may maintain or increase them, or even provoke an outbreak. The phobias are, in general, just as effective unconsciously as the urge to public display of the whole sexual organ or the member only to females of tender or mature age is irresistible. In the act of exhibition, the man frees himself from an obscure burden; yet the pleasurable feelings induced by this release do not necessarily lead to orgasm. When orgasm is not spontaneous or induced by masturbation, the exhibition tends to be repeated for hours in different places or in front of different people. Sadism and masochism are associated with exhibitionism but are far from being very marked in all cases.

There is, for instance, a type of MGE which could be described as "pillorism"—putting oneself in the pillory in a humiliating fashion. Moreover, exhibitionists sometimes suffer from a compulsion to be caught which imposes itself in spite of their conscious intentions, so that they fail to take elementary precautions or use to advantage opportunities of escape. In such cases, arrest leads to a mixture of despair and of relief. In favorable circumstances, it may lead to the initiation of effective treatment.

So much for masochism in MGE; sadism, and what I call the inhibitionism of exhibitionists, will be described later on in this chapter.

Genetically, the situation in MGE is not that there has been a failure properly to integrate the exhibitionistic components of the total sexuality of the infant nor that these components have been anarchically preserved. The exhibitions and displays which occur, like all sorts of other infantile sexual practices, yield no adequate understanding of MGE, even when they are strongly represented in the infantile sexual polymorphism; the latter, incidentally, is not as common as the writings of the older analysts would indicate. On the contrary, a characteristic feature of these cases is a loose sex life in a circle of children and young people of both sexes. There are, thus, definite departures from the norm both in the intensity and the amount of early sexual activity. A latency period worthy of the name is lacking. No particular constitution appears to be the decisive factor but, rather, a definite family constellation; the boy lacks the understanding love of parents or educators. In all events, I know of no case of a subsequent exhibitionist who grew up in a favorable or even harmonious environment. Often the parents are unhappily married; and the open or concealed conflict between them is associated with a relationship to the children made up of alternate neglect and cosseting, brutality and spoiling. With such parents, it is difficult for a happy relationship to exist among the children; instead, there are distrust and jealousy, with the result that the child takes sides between his parents, suspects himself of inferiority, and strives to improve his own position by sycophancy and tale-telling. There is probably a connection between this jealousy and pharisaism in the nursery and what I describe later as the "inhibitionism of exhibitionists."

The child's "belief in love" (Freud), with its significance for the development of the superego, tends to be despised and ill-used by the adults concerned, with the result that a police-like conscience rather than a genuine morality emerges while cowardice and impudence take the place of courage. Moreover, since the child's inclinations and gifts are not recognized or encouraged, his practical efficiency—and, with it, his self-confidence—suffers; later, his relations with the teachers and educators who take the parents' place are apt to be strained and clouded. As narcissistic occulsions and negative transferences make relations with the parental images difficult, the formation of an effective psychotherapeutic contact tends to be an extremely thorny problem, even when the exhibitionist comes to the analyst of his own accord without being ordered to undergo treatment by the courts.

MGE is thus a phenomenon of social psychopathology in its genesis as well as in its effects. Sufficient attention cannot be paid to the "family neurosis," the abnormal constellation, sometimes resulting in character malformation not just in one member of the family but in several, all taking the form of MGE. The peculiar nature of the exhibitionist is such that he may be entirely unaware of MGE among other members of his family. In view of all this, it is not impossible that there may be innate or hereditary factors in MGE of which we are at present unaware. But it is its social genesis that is immediately apparent and of practical importance.

In the earliest forms of his instinctual drives, the oral, the exhibitionist is tied to his mother; in the later forms of polymorphous sexuality, he is tied to childish and youthful, predominantly female objects. The "mama complex" aspects, described by E. Bergler and L. Eidelberg,[2] seem to me to be correct, though according to my limited experience the weaning trauma takes second place to the deprivation of maternal love and care. But the consequences in terms of frustration are the same—hatred of the mother and mother-images, with the familiar strong and extensive oral character traits. Whether the hatred of the father and the father images is substantially less, I am not in a position to decide. Only with the outbreak of MGE is the interest in the female breast displaced on to the exhibitionist's own genitals as a whole (not his penis only). Thus the genitals, because of an intensified secondary narcissism and a hypertrophy, not only of introjective identification but of the primary processes in general, carry the unconscious meaning of the female breast. (Here we have one of the chief causes of the "feminine character" of exhibitionists which has also been noted by nonanalytic observers.) Cannibalistic impulses, however, are projected on to the vagina, which is the object of intense fear, all sorts of infernal attributes being ascribed to it; or it is regarded as a trap, e.g., the vagina dentata; alternatively, this kolpophobia is concealed behind an apparent lack of interest in sexual intercourse and manifests itself in displaced form as claustrophobia, etc.

MGE is a post-pubertal and, even more often, a post-marital catastrophe; it is the consequence of a retarded psycho-sexual development. True, in the society of his contemporaries, the exhibitionist early demonstrates a lively instinctual life which continues for a considerable length of time. His heterosexual and homosexual relationships are differentiated by the fact that homosexuality, particularly directed toward grownups, rapidly changes into shyness and aggression. This prodrome may point to the symptom of "inhibitionism," in which an exhibitionist behaves toward other exhibitionists as if he were a gamekeeper and they poachers. In the heterosexual field, the exhibitionist may achieve sexual intercourse, but the more mature the female partner, the more rarely is this apt to occur. In short, there tends to be a premature attainment of the phallic stage, followed by no further advance in maturity.

It is this standstill, the failure to advance to the genital stage, that is the precondition for MGE; sexual intercourse acts like oil on the fire of pregenitality. Mutual touching of the genitals and many other pregenital features tend to be more pleasurable than sexual intercourse; coitus is a secondary thing, carried out more for the partner's sake; her desiring it can be as upsetting as her refusal. The latter is capable of leading to a mixture of rage and sexual frenzy which may be discharged in a sex act resembling rape. Wooing and waiting are not consistent with the exhibitionist's nature. Menstruation in particular is apt to upset him; it may not only disgust him but drive him to the strangest acts of aggression. The thirty-six-year-old V., for example, had the following dream while sleeping with his young wife, who was menstruating: "I wished to have sexual intercourse with an older woman. She irritated and angered me. I threw myself on top of her but my member absolutely refused to become stiff. This put me in a rage, an indescribably terrible rage, and I wanted to strangle the woman. But I did not catch her round the throat but under the breasts, and compressed her thorax. 'What are you doing?' she said. 'Have you gone mad?' I looked at her for a moment. She was my wife. . . . And then I awoke." An aviator dreamed that an aircraft crashed through the kitchen window of a restaurant and that he was flung out of the wreckage into the kitchen. His mangled, bleeding body lay by the oven and his head, crushed to a pulp, lay in a frying pan. He had to conduct a technical inspection of all this. As he was leaving, two friendly girls offered him the frying pan and, after rapidly overcoming his disgust, he enjoyed the contents.

Neither in my own cases nor in those reported in the literature on the subject have I ever observed that the sight of the female breasts had any special significance in stimulating the act of exhibition. But, before the onset of MGE, it is different. At this stage, sex appeal is most definitely attached to a shapely female bust. Repression of interest in the breasts may not be noticed if the "beautiful figure" or "shape" of a young woman or the plumpness of half-grown girls is mentioned. But it is, above all, the female legs which attract attention because of elegant stockings or good shape, particularly if more of them is accidentally disclosed. Underclothes, accidentally revealed by a gust of wind when cycling, for instance, are also important, as well as any partial nudity, but complete nakedness never. In particular, an exhibitionistic act can easily take place if the MGE, while urinating, sees an expression of interest in a female face.

Exhibitionists' marriages, like those of alcoholics (A. Im Obersteg[7]), tend to be "mother marriages," though in the case of the former the greater age of the wife does not tend to be so pronounced. None of the ten exhibitionists of whom I possess the comparative age figures had a wife very much younger than himself. When they were about the same age, the wife invariably created the impression of being older than her husband.

In case M, the wife was several years older than her husband; in case B, she was four years older and, in case A, eight years older. In such marriages, children are rivals; pregnancy and birth introduce an aggressive-phobic element into the marriage relationship and may lead to an outbreak of MGE. I know, by hearsay, of one single example of an exhibitionist's marriage which resulted in many children; this was in the rural conditions of central Switzerland. According to my own figures, of eight marriages—of from four to twenty-nine years' duration—five were childless and, in the remaining three, there was one child each. Transference to the exhibitionist's children of his unfavorable relationship to his siblings should be regarded as a factor contributing to this scarcity of children in exhibitionists' families.

Here are some more data about the onset of MGE. V. started

exhibiting at the age of thirty, having married at twenty-seven and a half. His MGE lasted for several years. But a first isolated outbreak had occurred in his eighteenth year after he had taken part in a gang burglary, had a terrible experience connected with menstruation, and served a six months' term in prison. T. first had sexual intercourse at eighteen and exhibited for the first time at twenty-one. Mario's loose instinctual life[4] led to proper sexual intercourse for the first time at eighteen and a half. His exhibitionism began at twenty-one. At twenty-five, he married, whereupon his exhibitionism was intensified and became established for twenty-five years, at the end of which he had himself castrated by operation. Mn. married at twenty-seven and started exhibiting at thirty-one. B. had a slight onset of exhibitionism at the age of eighteen and married at twenty-three. After being in hospital for many weeks because of "sciatica," he met his wife, who was menstruating, and on a cycling outing next day committed an act of MGE, to which he remained committed for many years.

A. had his first sexual relations at seventeen; between the ages of nineteen and twenty, he had an affair with a girl who was frigid and who disappointed, deceived and abandoned him. After this, he had a new pleasurable experience at seeing, from the parade ground at his recruits' training center, a woman cyclist with flying skirts; he went through an exhibitionistic phase between the ages of twenty-one and twenty-two. He married happily at the age of twenty-seven. After two or three months of marriage, there took place, without any manifest disturbance of the marriage, a fresh outbreak of exhibitionism, which soon led to his arrest. He was put on probation and came immediately for treatment. The urge to exhibit himself soon disappeared and, over a period of three years, there was no relapse.

In 1936, I described a particular form of rivalry between exhibitionists as the inhibitionism of exhibitionists.[4a] This frequent though not invariable symptom had eluded previous investigators, with the exception of M. Hirschfeld.[8a] Nothing of the kind is mentioned, for instance, by J. E. Staehelin[16] in his details of one hundred cases, which were, however, collected largely from the point of view of forensic psychiatry. The phenomenon I described as inhibitionism manifests itself in frightening off other exhibitionists and very often giving them away. The exhibitionist and inhibitionist phases never coincide. Either one or the other is practiced, not both together. But the exhibitionist phase always predominates; the inhibiting is practiced only occasionally though, in the course of years, it may recur again and again, particularly when the exhibitionist knows himself to be suspected by the police. Exhibitionists discover each other because they keep seeing each other at exhibitionistic "beats." For a considerable time, there is, of course, uncertainty whether the other man is an exhibitionist or a detective. Those who practice inhibiting generally do so silently, assuming the manner and behavior of a detective and confining themselves to an admonishing look which gives the suspect to understand that he is being watched. But sometimes words are exchanged with police patrols, whose attention is drawn to the suspect. I have seldom heard of inhibitionists catching exhibitionists in the act; they generally confine themselves to watching their rivals and silently causing them uneasiness.

The twenty-one-year-old T., an exhibitionist of Theophrastus' gross or buffoon type, took a grim pleasure in spying on R., another exhibitionist ten years older than himself, catching him in the act and handing him over to the police. The man whom we have previously referred to as Mario noticed, in the crowd at a *Schutzenfest*, an older man who was feeling women from behind, and had him arrested. In the physician's rooms, he took offense at a statue of a naked man and woman. He used to haunt the exhibitionistic "beats" and quarters of the town, sometimes in the guise of a detective. At others, oddly affected by one or other of the strangers who were known to him by sight, he would abandon his proposed exhibitionistic act, allow himself to be followed at a comfortable walking-pace from one beat to another—perhaps glancing back occasionally at his pursuer—until, at a suitable moment when he was unobserved, he took to headlong flight. The educated and well-read twenty-five-year-old exhibitionist S. based his animosity to other exhibitionists on the cleavage in himself and the girlish terror of exhibitionists displayed by the author of the *Diary of an Adolescent Girl*. Of the inhibitionism of exhibitionists he ironically observed: "The hostile attitude to exhibitionists does not seem to be confined to me. Judges in particular seem to be liable to it. Or are they in the last resort . . . ? After all, their position gives them enough opportunity of being in the limelight!" This joke recalls the contribution to the subject made by M. Hirschfeld, the only author who has mentioned this matter. He described, in 1928, how a well-dressed man in an otherwise empty compartment of a Berlin tram opened his coat in front of a young girl sitting opposite and terrified her by showing his naked and erect member. The girl called for help. The exhibitionist, in spite of his struggles and pleas, was seized by people from the next compartment and handed over to the police. To the astonishment of the latter, the arrested man turned out to be one of themselves, a police inspector known for his unusual severity toward exhibitionists.

In the course of years, I have come across all sorts of interconnections among the exhibitionists who became known to me. One of them, for instance, helped to get another arrested before himself falling victim to a third. Inhibitionism is the opposite of the collective fecal exhibitionism described by O. Reik, the gangs of youthful burglars who leave behind them *cartes de visites odorantes*. My exhibitionist V. has the misfortune, while himself in an exhibitionistic mood, to detect between the bushes in a public park another man obviously in a similar frame of mind. Standing there absorbed at the sight, he was surprised by two policemen who took him to the station angrily protesting his innocence. According to the police report, his fly-buttons were partially undone. At all events, he was convicted on this, as on many other similar occasions, though when he really exhibited himself he invariably escaped.

Since Freud's *Three Essays on the Theory of Sexuality*, it has been accepted analytically that every exhibitionist is also a *voyeur*. We shall not fail to recognize in inhibitionism a hostile scoptophilic attitude directed toward the same sex. A., my mildest case, like Mario in his preexhibitionist adolescent days, had homosexual approaches made to him and his companions by an adult stranger while bathing and reacted so violently that the homosexual was nearly drowned and had to be rescued by his enemies. Toward the end of his first exhibitionistic phase, A. noticed a *voyeur* kneeling in a woody hiding place watching a pair of lovers on a bench. He seized the man, who gave such a pitiful description of his kolpophobia—which permitted him sexual pleasure only at a distance, to the accompaniment of masturbation—that our exhibitionist let him go. This experience shook him to such an extent and was such a pointer to himself that he felt deeply ashamed of his exhibitionism; the shock helped to produce a far-reaching self-cure, a normalization which lasted for several years.

Related to the phenomenon described above is the mixture of exhibitionism and inhibitionism in a type of group behavior indulged in by both older and younger girls in the proletarian quarters of towns. These children smell out male genital exhibitionists and provoke them by obscene words and gestures while one of them quietly sneaks off to the police and has the man arrested.

The Syndrome of MGE as Exhibitionismus Sollicitus *in Contradistinction to Infantile* Exhibitio Sollicitans

I shall not attempt, as I did nearly twenty years ago,[4a] to indicate the difference between exhibition as a component activity of infantile polymorphous sexuality and the morbid addiction of MGE.

Childish exhibitionism, which is present in both boys and girls and is by no means limited to the genital area, takes place more or less by mutual consent and aims at contact, whether visual or manual; more or less secret games of "mothers" and "doctors" tend to be practiced accordingly. Childish exhibitionism is pleasurably seductive. I call it *exhibitio sollicitans* and not exhibitionism because it occurs sporadically and episodically; it is thus not a condition but a part of a total development, a component in a general trend, in contradistinction to the substitution of a part for the whole, which is what exhibitionism is. There is no doubt that infantile *exhibitio sollicitans* can be revived in maturity, be regressively reactivated, and appear in the form of exhibitionism. However, what I have hitherto described as MGE does not take the form of this childish play, though it may be remarked in passing that, in male exhibitionism, there are all sorts of transitional types between the *sollicitus* and the *sollicitans*. Psycho-organic changes, particularly those associated with old age, make room for *exhibitio sollicitans* and other childish types. Thus the exhibitionistic syndrome of so-called second childhood, the behavior of men who have become mentally defective with children whom they have bribed by presents, resembles the original *exhibitio sollicitans*. These few remarks will suffice here without going into further details.

The study of animal behavior (ethology) has produced a good deal of material related to *exhibitio sollicitans*. It speaks, for instance, of "sympathetic induction." The animal psychologist investigates innate releasing mechanisms (IRM) which can be set in motion by the sign stimuli of the animal's partner (N. Tinbergen[19]). In his *Comparative Morphology of Vertebrates*, A. Portmann[14] shows that the higher eutheria or, to use an older expression, the higher mammals are progressively differentiated from archaic forms, such as Amphioxus, primitive fish, etc., both by the head's being increasingly differentiated and marked off from the rest of the body and by the displacement of the gonads from the middle of the body toward the hindquarters and the development of the scrotum, i.e., a part of the body opposite to the head, an anal-genital pole of special shape and color.

It is surprising and amusing to observe that these discoveries in the field of animal development have their counterparts in the field of anthropology. Huizinga's *homo ludens* with his customs, clothing and fashions—of which plenty more could be said—does a great many things worthy of observation from the point of view of comparative psychology. Without going further into the social and psychological function of morphological and ethological developments in the animal world, we may recall the formal emphasis of the anal-genital pole among the higher animals which, in turn, recalls what I said about stage-fright-hare's-foot exhibitionism among actors. As a parallel to so-called zoological display, we may mention the creation of the top

hat fashion as described in an old copy of the *Hatter's Journal*
and quoted in *The Times* of London on November 11, 1926.
According to Brockhaus, the top hat developed from the round
hat of the French Revolution. According to the *Hatter's Journal*
of January 10, 1797, it was introduced as follows: "John
Hetherington, haberdasher, of the Strand, was arraigned before
the Lord Mayor yesterday on a charge of a breach of the peace
and inciting to riot, and was required to give bonds in the sum
of £500. It was stated in evidence that Mr. Hetherington, who
is well connected, appeared on the public highway wearing upon
his head what he called a silk hat (which was offered in
evidence), a tall structure having a shiny lustre, and calculated
to frighten timid people. As a matter of fact, the officers of the
Crown stated that several women fainted at the unusual sight,
while children screamed, dogs yelped, and a younger son of
Cordwainer Thomas, who was returning from a chandler's shop,
was thrown down by the crowd which had collected, and had
his right arm broken."

Exhibitionistic emphasis of the opposite pole of the body
by means of clothing and armor is demonstrated by the example
of the mercenaries mentioned earlier. This can be taken as, at
most, a border case of *exhibitio sollicitans*.

Hare's-foot exhibitionism on the stage, in spite of all its irony
—for a "hare's foot" denotes cowardice—shows characteristics
of what I call *exhibitio nismus sollicitus* in contradistinction to
exhibitio sollicitans. The Latin adjective *sollicitus* points to a
state of anxiety; *sollicitus* means restless, disturbed, excited,
worried, shy.

The distinction between the *sollicitans* and *sollicitus* types
of exhibition and exhibitionism is useful. It describes infantile
genital and total exhibition as *exhibitio sollicitans* while the
type which was recently described by H. Zulliger[22] as a

"special kind of infantile confession" (and was attributed many years ago by D. T. Burlingham[3] to a compulsion to confess and was called by J. Klaesi[12] a substitute for a guilty act) can be put down as *sollicitus*. With the latter, there also belong certain infantile and childish masochistic forms of enureses[4b] which can be described as pillorism.

The phobic-perverse syndrome of MGE can plainly be described as *exhibitio sollicitus*. This will serve as a protection against confusions, misunderstandings and simplifications which may easily arise from O. Fenichel's description of the phenomenon as a "simple hypertrophy of an infantile component instinct." It is remarkable that the anxiety in the behavior and actions of the male genital exhibitionist has hardly been noted. As mentioned earlier, the phobic element in MGE consists mainly, but not exclusively, of a kolpophobia which manifests itself in claustrophobias. To the sufferer from MGE, his own home is no home and his bed, even if he does not have to share it with his wife, is not a place of comfortable security. All the same—if he is not actually impotent—he prefers masturbating alone in his bed—if he believes he can do so undetected—to responding to his wife's needs of tenderness and sexuality. But he never exhibits in his own home, though particularly at the beginning of the disorder, he will exhibit out of it: from a window, balcony, etc. In by far the majority of cases, it is public places, passages and buildings and, in particular, what I have described as "beats"—public parks, gardens, walks and woods—which the exhibitionist frequents, whether on foot, on a bicycle or in a car. Lasègue[20] describes MGE as a *scandale privé plutôt qu'un outrage public*. In the context, he is merely emphasizing the difference between a morbid and a criminal action. It should, however, be said that public disapproval is a *sine qua non* for MGE, whether it is practiced in solitary or crowded places. In any case, the compulsion to exhibit is greater than the fear of the police and of the courts. Punishment brings little improvement or none at all. Exhibitionists have more than once told me that benevolent police inspectors have told them to practice their perversion, if they cannot give it up, at home instead of in public. But they are unable to do this because of the mainly unconscious but very effective claustrophobic reasons which we have mentioned.

Further light on the phobic element in MGE can be found in an autobiographical incident recorded by the German writer, Theodor Storm (1817-1888). At the age of six or seven, he made himself a stall out of an old sugar box and wanted goods to sell from it. "They were to be manufactured goods and, in view of the size of my stall, I needed a lot." The colored rags he needed were, however, kept by his mother under lock and key and, from her, unlike his always helpful grandmother, he expected only refusal. To his astonishment, however, that did not happen on this occasion. No sooner had the small boy plucked up the courage to put his request than his mother agreed and gave him all the colored rags he wanted. "I was completely bewildered in my childish head by this so sudden and overwhelming fulfillment of my wishes," he says. That night in bed, tired after his play, he wondered about the reason for his mother's unexpected kindness that day. A terrible certainty suddenly dawned on him as he lay there and pondered: his mother wanted to kill him. His grandmother came and found the boy in a state of terror. He "confessed" the reason to her— "confessed" is the word he uses—and it was only with difficulty that his grandmother and mother were able to soothe him.

This murder phantasy obviously arose in the boy as the result of frustrations, but the remarkable thing about it is less its projection on to the mother than the fact that it broke through only after the bad mother had turned into a good one.

Thus for transference and projection reasons, as manifested in their "mother-marriages," marital fulfillment in MGE is spoiled. In addition, there is a great deal that must remain unsaid about the fragile personality of exhibitionists.

If the phobic side of MGE derives from maternal soil, its libidinous symptomatology is rooted in loose infantile and childish sexual activity with contemporaries. There is a phobic element in the perverse symptomatology in MGE also. Thus intimate sexual experiences with a girl of the same age at the stage of puberty may be revived in an outbreak of exhibitionism in a man of thirty. The experience is not repeated intimately, however, but at a distance, i.e., it is reproduced in the form of an exhibitionistic act by the man of thirty in front of a young girl.

The exhibitionist's shyness is at a minimum in the presence of young girls though he knows that indecency with children involves extra-heavy penalties from the law. But if certain women, mistaking the *sollicitus* for the *sollicitans* aspect of MGE, take the act of the male genital exhibitionist as an invitation to closer contact, he is immediately put off. He wants no partnership but needs female spectators to increase his narcissism at their expense. Thus, by a retreat from object-libido, the male exhibitionist arrives in his act at a feeling of hermaphroditic self-fulfillment, a sense of "intoxication with his own power," as M. Bleuler says. L. Eidelberg[5] quotes an exhibitionistic text which no doubt has its variations. It says: "It is not true that I want to have breasts. The truth is that I am proud of having a penis. It is not true that I am interested in watching women who undress. The truth is that I want to show them my penis." But, as already mentioned, it is not just the penis but the whole sexual region which is engaged in the exhibitionist's attitude to femininity and women. Its meaning in a nutshell is: "I am you, all of you, and—whether you swallow it or not—still more." A certain relationship between this psychopathological meaning of exhibition and its older legal meaning is unmistakable.

REFERENCES

1 Bäumer, G. and Droescher, L. *Von der Kindesseele. (Beiträge zur Kinderpsychologie aus Dichtung und Biographie.* Gekürzte Ausgabe.) Third ed., Leipzig, 1918.

2 Bergler, E. and Eidelberg, L. *Internationale Zeitschrift für Psychoanalyse,* Vol. XIX, No. 4, 1933.

3 Burlingham, D. T. *Imago,* Vol. XX, 1934.

4 Christoffel, H. *International Journal of Psychoanalysis,* Vol. XVII, 1936.

———. "Trieb und Kultur." *Zur Sozialpsychologie, Physiologie und Psychohygiene der Harntriebhaftigkeit mit besonderer Berücksichtigung der Enuresis. Basle,* 1944.

5 Eidelberg, Ludwig. *An Outline of a Comparative Pathology of the Neuroses.* New York, 1954.

6 Fenichel, Otto. *Perversionen, Psychosen, Charakterstörungen.* (Psychoanalytische spezielle Neurosenlehre, Vol. II.) Vienna, 1931.

7 *Gesundheit und Wohlfahrt.* Vol. XXXII, 1952.

8 Hirschfeld, M. *Geschlechtskunde,* Vol. I. Stuttgart, 1930.

———. *Die Weltreise eines Sexualforschers.* Brugg, 1933.

9 Huizinga, J. *Homo Ludens.* Basle, 1944.

10 *Chin P'Ing Mei: The Adventurous History of Hsi Men and his Six Wives.* London, 1939.

11   Kinsey, A. C., W. B. Pomerey and C. E. Martin. *Sexual Behavior in the Human Male*. Philadelphia and London, 1948.

12   Klaesi, J. *Zeitschrift für die gesamte Neurologie und Psychiatrie*, Vol. XXXV, 1917.

13   Krauss, F. S. *Anthropophyteia*. (Jahrbücher für folkloristische Erhebungen, Vol. I, Südslavische Voksüberlieferungen, die sich auf der Geschlechtsverkehr beziehen.) Leipzig, 1904.

14   Portmann, A. *Einführung in die vergleichende Morphologie der Wirbeltiere*. Basle, 1948.

15   Reik, T. *Der unbekannte Mörder*. Vienna, 1932.

16   Staehelin, J. E. *Zeitschrift für die gesamte Neurologie und Psychiatrie*. 1926.

17   Teirich, H. *Psyche. Heidelberg*, 1953-54.

18   Theophrastus. *The Characters*. Trans. J. M. Edmonds. London, 1929.

19   Tinbergen, N. *The Study of Instinct*. London, 1950.

20   *L'Union Médicale*. Paris, 1877.

21   Van Wulfften-Palthe, P. M. *Internationale Zeitschrift für Psychoanalyse*, Vol. XXI, 1935.

22   Zulliger, H. *Praxis der Kinderpsychologie und Kinder-Phychiatrie*. 1953.

Fetishism: The Symbolic, the Imaginary and the Real

JACQUES LACAN AND
WLADIMIR GRANOFF

Fetishism has suffered, in psychoanalytical studies, a singular fate.

At the beginning of the century, in the first edition of *Three Essays on Sexuality*, Freud assigned to this practice a particular position in the study of neurosis and perversion.[1] This special place was re-emphasized in the second edition, where Freud further noted that the distinction—the contrast—which appeared to exist between fetishism and neurosis disappeared when fetishism itself was subjected to close study. Certainly, fetishism is classed as a perversion and a perversion is in turn—according to the well-known formula—the negative of a neurosis. Nonetheless, fetishism is one form of perversion where no contrast can be found with a neurosis.

Freud himself recommends the study of fetishism to all who wish to understand the fear of castration and the Oedipus complex. To the disciples of psychoanalysis as to its detractors, the importance given to the Oedipus complex has always been the touchstone of one's overall attitude toward analysis.

No effort, then, has been spared to call attention to the

265

importance of fetishism. With what result? The span between 1910 and the past few years was not overrich in studies on this theme; only half a dozen major contributions can be counted.

Freud returned twice to the subject at eleven-year intervals and, each time, in a very special way.[10,11] Reading his articles, one senses that Freud himself wondered whether people would really grasp what he was talking about.[11]

It is useful, in this connection, to remember that one of Freud's last unfinished fragments deals with fetishism. As during his lifetime he invariably set the new courses for analysis, it is not far-fetched to see in this article a prescience of the direction in which psychoanalytical thought was inevitably to turn in the period after the war.

To wit—the study of the ego. For in the psychoanalytical studies of the past ten years—however they may differ in accordance with varying traditions, tastes, predilections, styles and psychoanalytical schools in each country—the study of the ego is certainly the primary preoccupation.[6,24]

During the same period, works on fetishism have reappeared. For, as Freud recommended, the study of fetishism is and remains most illuminating for anyone who would concentrate upon the Oedipean dynamic in order more fully to understand what the ego is.

To clarify our ideas as well as to indicate the main orientation of our paper, we must first recall that psychoanalysis, which permits us to see farther into the psyche of children than any other science, was discovered by Freud through the observation of adults—more precisely, by listening to them or, rather, to their speech. Indeed, psychoanalysis is a "talking cure."

To recall such generally accepted truths may at first seem an imposition; upon reflection, it is not. It is only a reminder of an essential methodological point of reference. For, unless we are to deny the very essence of psychoanalysis, we must make use of language as our guide through the study of the so-called pre-verbal structures.[20]

Freud has shown us and taught that symptoms speak in words, that, like dreams, they are constructed in phrases and sentences.

In his article of 1927, Freud introduced us to the study of the fetish by indicating that it has to be deciphered, and deciphered like a symptom or a message.[10] He tells us even in what language it has to be deciphered. This way of presenting the problem is not without significance. From the beginning, such an approach places the problem explicitly in the realm of the search for meaning in language rather than in that of vague analogies in the visual field. (Such as, for example, hollow forms recalling the vagina, furs the pubic hairs, etc.) From "Glanz auf der Nase" to the female penis, passing through "Glance on the Nose," the passage is strictly incomprehensible unless one has stuck to the path which Freud indicated. At the entrance of this path stands an inscription which reads, "What is its *meaning?*"

The problem is not one of repressed affects; the affect in itself tells us nothing. The problem concerns the denegation of an idea. With this denegation, we find ourselves in the realm of significance, the only area where the key word "displacement" has significance. A fundamental province of human reality, the realm of the imaginary.[10]

It is here that little Harry takes his stand, from the moment his famous visitor enters, when he cuts off the hands of children—so they will not scratch—their noses, or when he gives this appendage to the caterpillars to devour.[22]

It is thus that Freud classifies this behavior when, dealing with "transformations during puberty" in the *Three Essays*, he tells us that the choice of the object takes place in the form of creatures of the imagination. He is speaking of a metabolism of

images when he explains the return to pathological characteristics, under the influence of ill-fated love, by the return of the
libido to the image of the person beloved during childhood.

Such is the profound meaning of the remark about the
psychic contribution to perversions. The more repellent the
perversion, the more clearly this participation is revealed. "No
matter how horrifying the result, an element of psychological
activity can always be found which corresponds to the *idealization* of the sexual tendency."

Where, then, is the break in this line? What occurs at the
moment when—ceasing to imagine, to speak, to draw—Harry,
without knowing why, cuts off a lock of hair? At the moment
when, without explanation, he runs away screaming in order
not to see the crippled friend?

At first glance, we would say that he no longer *knows* what
he is *doing*. We are now in a dimension where meaning seems
lost, the dimension where is to be found, apparently, the fetishist
perversion, the taste for shiny noses. And, if there were no
elaboration upon the nose or the amputated lock of hair, this
would be as impossible to analyze as a true perverse fixation.
Indeed, if a slipper were, strictly speaking, the displacement of
the female organ and no other elements were present to
elaborate primary data, we would consider ourselves faced with
a primitive perversion completely beyond the reach of analysis.[19]

It follows that the imaginary does not, in any sense, represent
the whole of what can be analyzed. The clinical observation
of Harry may well help us to resolve the question we have
set ourselves. For this is the only time that Harry's behavior
displays what, in clinical psychiatry, we would call reticence,
opposition, mutism. He no longer tries to express himself in
words; he screams. He has thus twice given up the attempt to
make himself understood by others.

And it is here that the break occurs.

What is the register in which, for a moment, this child refuses to place himself? We would say, with E. Jones, the register of the symbol—a register essential to human reality.[9]

If Harry no longer makes himself understood by others, he has by the same token become incomprehensible to them. This may seem a remarkably banal observation but it is so only if we forget that, when we say, "You are my wife," we are also saying, "I am your husband," and are thus ourselves no longer the same as we were before speaking these words. Speech is subtle stuff, yes; but, in this case, it is an offering. In this giving, analysis finds its *raison d'être* and its effectiveness.[20]

And if we consider mankind's first words, we note that the password, for instance, has the function—as a sign of recognition—of saving its speaker from death.[21]

The word is a gift of language and language is not immaterial. It is subtle matter, but matter nonetheless. It can fecundate the hysterical woman, it can stand for the flow of urine or for excrement withheld.[6] Words can also suffer symbolic wounds. We recall the "Wespe" with a castrated W, when the wolf man realized the symbolic punishment which was inflicted upon him by Grouscha.[13]

Language is thus the symbolic activity *par excellence*; all theories of languages based on a confusion between the word and its referent overlook this essential dimension. Does not Humpty Dumpty remind Alice that he is master of the word, if not of its referent?

The imaginary is decipherable only if it is rendered into symbols. Harry's behavior at this moment is not; rather, he is himself drawn in by the image. Harry does not imagine the symbol; he gives reality to the image. This imaginary captation (*captation of and by the image*) is the essential constituent of any imaginary "reality," to the extent that we consider the latter as instinctive. Thus the same colors captivate the male and the female stickleback and draw them into the nuptial dance.

It is when, in analysis, the patient places himself in a narcissistic posture that we recognize we have struck the resistance. And what experience in analysis proves (and meets) is precisely that, instead of giving reality to the symbol, the patient attempts to constitute *hic et nunc*, in the experience of the treatment, that imaginary point of reference which we call bringing the analyst into his game.[20] This can be seen in the case of the rat man's attempt to create, *hic et nunc* with Freud, this imaginary anal-sadistic relationship; Freud clearly observes that this is something which betrays and reveals itself on the patient's face by what he refers to as "the horror of pleasure unknown."[12]

Such are the spheres in which we move in analysis. But are we in the same sphere when, in everyday life, we meet our fellow man and render psychological judgments about him? Are we in the same sphere when we say that so-and-so has a strong personality? Certainly not. Freud does not speak in the register of analysis when he refers to "the personalities" of the rat man. It is not on this level that we find the kind of possibility of direct appreciation and measurement which enables us to establish a given relationship with a given person.

We must admit this direct judgment of the person is of little importance in the analytical experience. It is not the real relationship that constitutes the proper field of analysis. And if, in the course of analysis, the patient brings in the phantasy of the analyst's fellatio, we will not try, despite the incorporative character of this phantasy, to fit it into the archaic cycle of his biography—for example, by attributing it to undernourishment in childhood. The idea would probably not occur to us. We would say, rather, that the patient is prey to phantasy. It may represent a fixation at a primitive oral stage of sexuality. But this would not induce us to say that the patient is a constitutional fellator. The imaginary element has only a symbolic value, which is to be appreciated and understood in the light of the particular moment of the analysis when it occurs. This phantasy is created to express itself, to be spoken, to symbolize something which may have an entirely different meaning at another moment in the dialogue.

It no longer surprises us when a man ejaculates at the sight of a shoe,[1] a corset, a mackintosh;[6] yet we would be very surprised indeed if any one of these objects could appease the hunger of an individual, no matter how extreme. It is just because the economy of satisfactions implied in neurotic disturbances is less bound to fixed organic rhythms—though it may direct some of them—that neurotic disturbances are reversible.

It is easy to see that this order of imaginary satisfaction can only be found in the realm of sexuality. The term "libido" refers to a concept which expresses this notion of reversibility and implies that of equivalence. It is the dynamic term which makes it possible to conceive a transformation in the metabolism of images.

Therefore, in speaking of imaginary satisfaction, we are thinking of something highly complex. In the *Three Essays,* Freud explains that instinct is not simple data but is rather composed of diverse elements which are dissociated in cases of perversion.[9] This conception of instinct is confirmed by the recent research of biologists studying the instinctual cycles, in particular, the sexual and reproductive cycles.

Aside from the more or less uncertain and improbable studies dealing with neurological relays of the sexual cycle—incidentally, the weakest point in these studies—it has been demonstrated that, in animals, these cycles are subject to displacement. Biologists have been able to find no word other than displacement to designate the sexual mainspring of symptoms.

The cycle of sexual behavior can be initiated in the animal by a certain number of starters. And a certain number of displacements can occur in the interior of the cycle.* Lorenz's studies show the function of the image in the feeding cycle. In man, it is also principally on the sexual plane that the imaginary plays a role and that displacements occur.

We would say, then, that behavior can be called imaginary when its direction to an image, and its own value as an image for another person, renders it displaceable out of the cycle within which a natural need is satisfied.

Animals are capable, in those displaced segments, of sketching out the rough lines of symbolical behavior, as for example, in the wagging dance, the language of bees. Behavior is symbolic when one of these displaced segments takes on a socialized value. It serves the group as reference point for collective behavior.

This is what we mean when we say that language is symbolic behavior *par excellence*.

If Harry remains silent, it is because he is in no state to symbolize. Between imaginary and symbolic relationships there is the distance that separates anxiety and guilt.[11]

And it is here, historically, that fetishism is born—on the line of demarcation between anxiety and guilt, between the two-sided relationship and the three-sided one. Freud does not fail to notice this when he recommends the study of fetishism to whoever may doubt the fear of castration; in the notes following the *Three Essays*, he says that perversions are the residue of development toward the Oedipus complex. For

---

* For example, in a struggle among birds, one of the fighters may suddenly begin to smooth his feathers; thus an aspect of parade behavior interrupts the cycle of combat.

it is here that the various elements of which instinct is composed may become dissociated.[9]

Anxiety, as we know, is always connected with a loss—i.e., a transformation of the ego—with a two-sided relation on the point of fading away to be superseded by something else, something which the patient cannot face without vertigo. This is the realm and the nature of anxiety.

As soon as a third person is introduced into the narcissistic relationship, there arises the possibility of real mediation, through the intermediary, of the transcendant personage, that is to say, of someone through whom one's desire and its accomplishment can be symbolically realized. At this moment, another register appears, that of law—in other words, of guilt.

The entire clinical history of Harry's case turns upon this point. Will the fear of castration thrust him into anxiety? Or will it be faced and symbolized as such in the Oedipal dialectic? Or will the movement rather be frozen in the permanent memorial which, as Freud puts it, fear will build for itself?[10]

To stress the point: if the *strength* of the *repression* (of the affect) is to be found in the *interest* for the successor of the feminine phallus, it is the denegation of its absence which will have constructed the memorial. The fetish will become the vehicle both of denying and asseverating the castration.

It is this oscillation which constitutes the very nature of the critical moment. To realize the difference of the sexes is to put an end to play, is to accept the three-sided relationship. Here, then, is Harry's vacillation between anxiety and guilt. His vacillation in his object-choice and, by the same token, later, in his identification.[22]

He caresses the shoes of his mother and of Sandor Lorand. It is his oscillation between the treatment inflicted to caress or to cut. It is the search for a compromise between his desires and his guilt which provides his mother with a penis. For he has explored her, and he knows she has none.[3,4,23] It is to the extent that the evidence forces itself upon him that, in his drawings, penises become longer and stronger. The denial of the vagina is necessary, according to Sandor Lorand, for the conservation of the happy triangle. Happy, yes—but, as Lorand would probably agree, not true. The true triangle means conflict. And here is where Harry falters.

Every analyzable—that is to say symbolically interpretable—situation is always inserted in a three-sided relationship.[5] Therefore, Freud had some reason to give this particular place to fetishism in his speculation. We have seen it in the structure of speech, which is mediation between individuals in libidinal realization.

What is shown in analysis is asserted by doctrines and demonstrated by experience—to wit—that nothing can be interpreted except through the intermediary of the Oedipal realization.[5] That is why it appears vain to explain the horror of female genitalia by certain visual memories dating from the painful passage through the birth canal.

For it is reality in its accidental aspect which stops the gaze of a child just before it is too late. There would certainly be no reason for the child to believe the threat of his nurse had he not seen the vulva of his little friend.[11] Nor is there any reason for him to accept the absence of the maternal penis, especially since he has narcissistically evaluated his own and has seen the even greater penis of his father, if he is unaware of the danger of losing it.[22]

This means that all two-sided relationships are always stamped with the style of the imaginary. For a relation to assume its symbolic value, there must be the mediation of a third person which provides the transcendent element through which one's relation to an object can be sustained at a given distance.[5,19]

If we have attached so much importance to the case of little Harry, it is because we feel that this case of fetishism is extremely enlightening. It articulates, in a particularly striking manner, those three realms of human reality which we have called the symbolic, the imaginary and the real.

For our part, we find here a further justification for the particular place which, as we noted at the beginning, Freud accords to the study of fetishism.*

REFERENCES

Abraham, Karl.
1 "Remarks on the Psychoanalysis of a Case of Foot and Corset Fetishism" (1910). *Selected Papers*. London, 1927.

2 "Mental After-Effects Produced in a Nine-Year-Old Child by the Observation of Sexual Intercourse Between Its Parents" (1913). *Selected Papers*. London, 1927.

3 "An Infantile Theory of the Origin of Female Sex" (1923). *Selected Papers*. London, 1927.

4 "An Infantile Sexual Theory Not Hitherto Noted" (1925). *Selected Papers*. London, 1927.

5 "Zwei Beiträge zur Symbolforschung—Dreiweg in der Oedipus-Sage." *Imago*, Vol. IX, 1925.

Dugmore, Hunter.
6 "Object-Relation Changes in the Analysis of a Fetichist." *International Journal of Psychoanalysis*, Vol. XXXV, 1954.

Fenichel, Otto.
7 "Some Infantile Sexual Theories Not Hitherto Described." *International Journal of Psychoanalysis*, Vol. V, 1928.

8 "On Transvestism" (1930). *The Psycho-Analytic Reader*. New York, 1948.

* We wish to express our grateful acknowledgment to Mr. and Mrs. Stanley Cleveland for their kind assistance in editing our English text.

Freud, Sigmund.
9 *Three Contributions to the Theory of Sex* (1905). New York, 1910.

10 "Fetishism" (1927). *International Journal of Psychoanalysis*, Vol. IX, 1928.

11 "Splitting of the Ego in the Defensive Process" (1938). *International Journal of Psychoanalysis*, Vol. XXII, 1941.

12 "L'homme aux Rats." *Cinq Psychanalyses.*

13 "L'homme aux Loups." *Cinq Psychanalyses.*

Granoff, Wladimir.
14 *Contribution à l'étude du fétichisme.* Paris, 1952.

Jones, Ernest.
15 *Papers on Psychoanalysis.* New York, 1913.

Lacan, Jacques.
16 "La famille." *Encyclopédie Française*, 1938. (Encyclopedia article)

17 "Le stade du miroir comme formateur de la fonction du de, telle qu'elle nous est révelée dans l'experience psychanalytique." *Revue française de psychanalyse*, Vol. IX, 1949.

18 "Some Reflections on the Ego." *International Journal of Psychoanalysis*, Vol. XXXIV, Part 1, 1953.

19 "Le Symbolique, l'Imaginaire et le Réel." (Conference report, 1953)

20 "Fonction et champ de la parole et du langage en psychanalyse." (Conference report, Instituto di Psychologia della Universita di Roma, 1953)

Strauss, Claude.
21 Les Structures élémentaires de la Parenté. Paris, 1947.

Lorand, Sandor.
22 "Fetishism in Statu Nascendi." *International Journal of Psychoanalysis*, Vol. XI, 1930.

Mac Brunswick, Ruth.
23 "A Note on the Childish Theory of Coitus a Tergo." *International Journal of Psychoanalysis*, Vol. X, 1929.

Payne, Sylvia.
24 "Some Observations on the Ego Development of the Fetishist." *International Journal of Psychoanalysis*, Vol. XX, 1939.

V

Therapy

Analysis of a Case
of a Male Homosexual

LUDWIG EIDELBERG

Mr. Wurmer had been in analysis with me for three years, having come originally because of legal difficulties connected with his manifest homosexuality. In these three years, he had changed considerably. His sexual interest in men and his fear of women had disappeared. The analytic material which he had produced showed a strong pre-Oedipal fixation to the oral stage, identification with the phallic mother and a defense against women by displacement of his libido on to men.

As in most cases of manifest homosexuality, the patient had no interest in women at the beginning of his treatment. After a few months of analysis, he began to realize that his lack of interest was a mask, hiding his hatred of women. This hate was due to traumatic experiences in the oral stage and was directed toward the female breasts. With the help of his dreams and their analysis, he realized that he had suffered from an unconscious breast envy and that the men he was in love with represented, unconsciously, women who were deprived of their breasts. In order to prove that he had no interest in breasts, his penis and the penis of the other man became the object of his sexual desire. While in that way the penis became vitally important, it represented unconsciously the female breast he was deprived of. Being sucked, and sucking the penis of the other man, meant being mother and infant at the same time.

The fact that his partner "looked like him" and that he did not need women, whose breasts and vagina mobilized his envy, helped him to keep his infantile idea of being self-sufficient. His analysis became really possible only after we succeeded in destroying his illusion of infantile omnipotence.

Something similar takes place in most cases of overt female homosexuality. The homosexual woman appears to suffer from an unconscious penis envy. She avoids men as sexual partners because she does not want to acknowledge that she needs their penis for her gratification. This penis which she rejects represents, unconsciously, the breast of the mother which she wants to destroy. Her positive interest in female love objects represents a defense against her hostility against the pre-Oedipal mother: "It is not true that I hate and want to destroy the female breasts. The truth is that I love and adore them."

The account of Mr. Wurmer's analysis is so typical that it does not deserve presentation except in a seminar for beginners. Only the final few months of his treatment will, perhaps, be of interest to advanced students of psychoanalysis.

At this stage of his treatment, Mr. Wurmer was having an affair with a girl who loved him very much and whom he liked. He seemed to have normal sexual relations and regarded his climax as superior to that which he used to have in his homosexual relations. It was difficult to say whether his rather cool attitude toward his girl friend was pathological and could, therefore, be changed by analysis. Not being able to measure the emotions of our patients, it is very difficult to say how much emotional involvement should be regarded as normal.

However, independently of the lack of such a quantitative approach, I had the impression that the quality of his attachment was narcissistic in nature. The patient had accepted and "forgiven" his girl friend's lack of penis. He even seemed to have lost his envy of her breasts and was prepared to be content without insisting on being man and woman, child and mother, at the same time. But, in spite of his success in his business and the satisfactory love affair with his girl friend, he did not appear to be happy.

Not being able to prove to the patient that he used his girl friend as an extension of his own body (and refrained from using her as an independent external object), I was already prepared to interrupt his treatment and wait for some change in the external reality which would make him more accessible. Just at this time, a dream occurred which perturbed him. In this dream, he was sucking the breasts of his girl friend and he felt the taste of urine coming from her breasts. The interpretation of this dream, which he described as a nightmare, showed that the breasts of his girl friend represented his own penis. In spite of the fact that the oral material had already been worked through, and that his interest in men had disappeared after he had recognized that their penis represented and denied his fixation to the breast, this additional piece of evidence appeared to have caused a great emotional response.

The fact that his penis represented the loved and hated breasts seemed to have become clearer now than before. During the analysis of his oral stage of development, I had represented his pre-Oedipal mother and his transference to me contained both love and hate. When this material was worked through, his intense fear of women and his disgust with the female breast decreased to such an extent that he was able to have sexual intercourse with the girl who was "in love" with him before he had started his analytic treatment. It appeared now that his therapeutic progress had caused us to overlook an important stage in his development; it was the period when his infantile desires were turned inward upon himself, before he succeeded in accepting his younger brother as his love object. Consequently, his self-centered love and hate had escaped the attention it deserved and was projected on to his girl friend. As she no longer represented his pre-Oedipal mother, he was able to meet her without fear but, as long as she represented himself, his reaction to her remained narcissistic. While it is true that, in so-called normal love, the representation of the external object is cathected not only with objectual but also with narcissistic libido, this patient's objectual libido belonged to an infantile stage.

From the technical point of view, it became necessary to show him that his interest in his girl friend was not only genital but partly phallic. The fact that he was able to have erections and an emission obscured his lack of mature genital development. Whereas in other cases, the phallic fixation may produce impotence, in this case the phallic fixation prevented the patient from developing a mature love.

When we have to explain to a patient something he has never experienced, we often feel as if we were talking about colors to a blind person. However, in this case, the dream supplied the weapon necessary to break through this part of his resistance. Independent of the intensity of his love, he was able to experience the fact that, in his dream, the breast contained urine, showing him that there must be something wrong, inasmuch as such an anticipation indicates not only that he is looking for a penis but that his relation to his girl friend is bound to produce disappointment and frustration in consequence. In this connection, the analysis of his infantile omnipotence, on which we had worked before, became necessary again. In the beginning of his treatment, his inability to admit that he was not the master of his own body and its desires, that they were not his servants but sometimes even his enemies, made his analysis very difficult. Before any change in his homosexuality could be attempted, he had to learn that his wishes could not be eliminated by will power alone. Part of this infantile omnipotence had been dealt with in his analysis. Now, in connection with his dream and the associations he produced, it became evident that the external objects he accepted represented, unconsciously, his own body. This defense mechanism appeared to be responsible for the fact that he remained so detached.

Anybody who expects an external object to behave as if this external object were a part of his own body is bound to be disappointed, even if this external object is fully devoted to him. Consequently, to protect himself against the shock of such a disappointment, the patient becomes detached. Before he can bear to fall in love with somebody else besides himself, he has to realize that he is no longer a little infant who cannot exist without mother and her continuous care of him.

To be more specific, this patient's girl friend represented his penis and he loved her, partly, in the way a normal man loves his own body. The fact that she was absolutely devoted to him made the illusion that she was part of him possible. In analysis, it became necessary to destroy this idea and to help him realize that his girl friend, although very much in love with him, was not his penis but a creature on her own account. I am not sure that this task would have been accomplished if an accident had not taken place which forced him to realize the limitations of his own power. One day his girl friend was run over by a bus and died. The patient developed a depression and the suffering connected with it helped us to obtain the material needed to free him completely from the results of his oral fixation. His depression was caused by his unconscious aggression which was turned against himself after the death of his girl friend. He could not forgive her for having died and left him. He suffered from a feeling of insecurity caused by this accident. If such a thing could happen, although he had done nothing to provoke it, how could I expect him to continue to live, to love and to hope? Furthermore, as his girl friend was dead, whom should he punish for this accident and how should he do it? Like other cases of depression in which oral material is involved, the death of his beloved meant, since she had represented part of him, the death of himself.

At this stage of his analysis, the danger of suicide was great. Not being able to destroy his girl friend, he had to destroy somebody else, perhaps himself. Many hours were spent, during which the patient blamed himself for not having loved his girl friend enough and in which he claimed that she would have been more careful, and thus have avoided being hit by the bus, if he had loved her more. In order to cure the patient, it became necessary to show him that his self-accusation was based on an illusion. While it was true that he could have made his girl friend happier when she was alive, there was no reason to assume that the accident was an unconscious suicide, caused by a lack of love.

This patient, like most depressed patients, was not relieved by being freed from this accusation. On the contrary, he resented having to admit that she had injured him by her death and that he had no power to avenge himself. One day he got so angry when I tried to explain this point to him that he interrupted me by saying, "I miss very much your previous silence!" Suicide appeared to him as the only way out of his dilemma. Not being able to punish his girl friend, he wanted at least to punish me. I did not deny that he had the power to hurt me by committing suicide but I tried to show him that the use of this power in such a destructive way would deprive him of it "for good."

The patient remained alive, recovered from his depression and, after a time, was lucky enough to find another girl. In this new relationship, his previous narcissistic interest in the object had been eliminated and he was able to establish a relationship which most of us would consider normal.

The analysis of this patient was terminated a few years ago and, according to my information, he has remained healthy.

From a technical point of view, the analysis of an overt homosexual, like the analysis of other perverts, should not neglect the problem of unconscious infantile omnipotence. In addition to the conscious feeling of superiority which many perverts exhibit, we also find the presence of an increased infantile megalomania. It is necessary to explain to such patients that their acceptance of their perversion and their fear of external punishment may protect them from the recognition that, independently of the attitude of the external world, part of their own unconscious personality resents the solution of perversion. In this case, I tried to explain to the patient, before he started his free associations, that some homosexuals approve of their choice of the love object because they are unconsciously afraid of not being able to change their attitude, even if they should discover that they disapprove of it. I described examples of symptom neurotics who resented their symptoms but were unable to eliminate them. I said that he, the homosexual, might appear to be better off because he avoids this kind of self-criticism. On the other hand, granted that psychoanalysis may help the symptom neurotic to dispose of his symptom, the symptom neurotic may be better off.

The patient admitted that the idea of resenting his homosexuality—being disgusted with it or feeling guilty because of it—did not appeal to him. He asked whether I was disgusted at having to treat a homosexual. I assured him that this was obviously not the case; if it were, I would not be able to analyze homosexuals. His perversion was not different nor worse than other perversions or neurotic character traits I had analyzed. He had come to me, obviously, in order to free himself from his homosexuality; as I assumed that he would be happier with a heterosexual love object—regarding his perversion as a result of unconscious defense mechanisms—I was eager to help him. As for the feeling of guilt, as long as it was used in a constructive manner, helping him to discover the unconscious factors responsible for his perversion, it could be regarded as helpful. On the other hand, the feeling of guilt could be used for a destructive attack on the self and employed in the provocation of external punishments.

In order to make analysis possible, it was necessary for him to have the courage to admit that he was not happy with himself, even if he had to wait for unconscious material in order to change those aspects of himself which he disliked. The idea that one should avoid self-criticism and maintain a united front against external authorities made sense only as long as he was so weak, and the external world so hostile, that no split in his own ranks could be tolerated. The recognition that he disapproved of some part of his personality did not mean that others had to be notified about it and, in that way, become able to humiliate him. The external authorities were no longer omniscient; there was no reason why he should not keep his secrets. I explained to the patient that we are usually able to obtain analytic material when the patient begins to suspect that what he does fails to make sense and becomes curious about the unconscious mechanisms responsible for his irrational behavior.

As long as the patient remains convinced that his interest in men represents the expression of a basic need, the analytical chances of understanding his behavior are small. I suggested that his lack of interest in women might be caused by an unconscious hate of women, not by the genuine lack of a heterosexual drive. Although the patient had been, for a time, platonically in love with a girl who seemed to be very much interested in him, he was honest enough to enumerate a few women whom he hated very much. When he recognized that this hatred was caused by an unconscious fear of women, the analysis of his lack of interest in them became possible.

The analysis of his infantile megalomania started after he understood intellectually that the amount of power he seemed to require was not really needed. He became interested in examining his illusion of omnipotence when he realized that complete control of the external world would result in the loss of some pleasure. Using, as an example, the act of breathing —in which we have a continuous supply of the oxygen we need —I pointed out that by not having to search for oxygen, store it or fight for it, we are deprived, as a rule, of the pleasure breathing might give us.

I am often asked by my students whether I give orders or prohibitions to homosexuals. I do not. Instead, I tell the patient that analysis is possible only if he tries consciously to be cured. The patient suffering from agoraphobia will, therefore, try to cross the street after he has gained some insight into the structure of his neurosis. A manifest homosexual, after he has recognized that his perversion may represent a denial of his fear of women, will consequently avoid homosexual intercourse and try to meet girls. Such conscious attempts will not cure him but they will increase his unconscious tension and produce analytical material.

Furthermore, the patient's efforts should stem from his own decision; that will make him proud of what he attempts whereas obeying an order would only humiliate him. If I decide that any particular patient does not try hard enough and that the probability of his cure is therefore remote, I feel free to terminate his treatment in order to save his time and mine.

In dealing with the conscious feeling of superiority which many perverts show, it is necessary to explain to the patient that all the famous men he cites as examples did not become famous because of their perversion. The experience of most analysts in the analysis of perverts does not indicate that the elimination of the perversion paralyzes their ability to sublimate. The opposite appears to be the case. However, the handling of unconscious infantile omnipotence, important in each analysis, appears to be of special significance in a case of perversion. The idea that one may play two roles at the same time, either by masturbation or by selecting a partner who represents the self, seems to be the result of an unconscious fear of not being able to survive after being cut off from the parents. It is my opinion that, in manifest homosexuality, the identification and the fixation on the pre-Oedipal mother is especially important. The phallic and the anal material present in such cases should not be regarded as trivial or banal and no short cut to the examination of the oral stage should be attempted. Nor should the experience we have gained in the treatment of other homosexuals nor the findings communicated to us by our colleagues cause us to neglect the study of the concrete material a particular patient offers. In other words, knowledge should not blind us to new discoveries. One may say, perhaps, that, in analyzing a patient, we should be as naïve as possible and suppress for a time what we have learned from other cases. Our ability to recognize in the new patient what we have heard described before no doubt helps us to proceed with our work, but this knowledge should not be used *instead* of examination of the concrete material presented to us by the patient on the couch.

REFERENCES

Freud, Anna. "Some Clinical Remarks Concerning the Treatment of Cases of Male Homosexuality." *International Journal of Psychoanalysis*, Vol. XXX, 1949.

Deutsch, Helene. "On Female Homosexuality." *Psychoanalytic Quarterly*, Vol. I, 1932.

Bibring, Grete. "Über eine orale Komponente bei männlicher Inversion." *Internationale Zeitschrift für Psychoanalyse*, Vol. XXV, 1940.

Eidelberg, Ludwig. "On the Theory and Treatment of Perversions," "A Contribution to the Study of Masochism," "A Contribution to the Study of the Masturbation Phantasy," all in *Studies in Psychoanalysis*. New York, 1948.

———. "Better Than the Love of Women," and "Her Master's Voice," in *Take Off Your Mask*. New York, 1948.

———. "Perversions." *An Outline of a Comparative Pathology of the Neuroses*." New York, 1954.

———. "Neurosis—A Negative of Perversion?" *Psychiatric Quarterly*, Vol. XXVIII, 1954.

The Therapy of Perversions

SANDOR LORAND

Just as no one specific reason or situation can be pointed out as responsible for any perversion, so no one unique and universal therapeutic procedure may be prescribed.

A unified theory about sexual perversion, its infantile origin and its vicissitudes in the early development of the individual were described for the first time by Freud in the *Three Essays on the Theory of Sexuality*. Freud studied infantile sexuality and manifest sexual perversion in detail; his work constituted the first important step toward the understanding of perversions from the analytical point of view. He described "polymorphous perversion," "auto-eroticism," "narcissism" and "fixation" in development, and their role in causing deviations in sexual development and, later, homosexuality.

This initial formulation of Freud's underwent many modifications and expansions, both at his own hands and at the hands of other early writers on perversion. These early contributors include Ferenczi, Abraham, Sachs and Jones; in the early years of analysis, they elaborated Freud's concept of perversion, especially the therapeutic aspect.

Freud suggested that the nucleus of perverse sexuality lies in the Oedipus complex; a large number of present-day analysts are still in agreement with this basic proposition. Although they recognize the fact that perverse sexuality is a complex problem, the starting point of their therapeutic attempts is always the Oedipus complex; however, they also regard castration anxiety, guilt, aggressive drives and the pregenital phases of development as contributing to the conflicts in perversions.

In female homosexuality, the central problem is considered by some to be the conflicts over penis envy but this is rather an oversimplification. I am sure that many analysts would agree with my opinion that perversions present *a wide range of clinical symptoms and that no specific concept of classification, etiology or psychodynamics has been established so far.*

Since perversions are, without exception, a mixture of perverse manifestation and neurotic symptom, patients who come for treatment because of their perversions do not come solely for that reason. They come because of the various degrees of anxiety, unhappiness, dissatisfaction and depressive moods connected with their perversions. It is true that all these anxieties can generally be considered as fear of castration and that the patients' perverse practices aim at a defense against and a denial of the castration fear.

The investigation and appreciation of the complexity of the symptomatology of perversion influences our therapeutic techniques. We have to be ready to modify our therapeutic approaches to the various types of perversions.

When treating such persons, it is always important to keep in mind that they did not originally start out to seek gratification by perverse manipulations. In the early period of development, there was normal sexual functioning and heterosexual experiences and phantasies though there may have been intrapsychic conflicts present at a very early age. This apparently normal functioning may have lasted through puberty and partially through adolescence. This is the basis on which to found our therapy, namely, an investigation of when their turn to homosexuality or other perverse gratifications occurred; then we trace the disorder back to its early roots, when conflicts about sexual objects first appeared, and try to find out the reasons for the distorted development.

Of major etiological importance in perversions is the oral phase of development. Glover, Ella Sharpe and the author, in the early years after the publication of Freud's paper on fetishism, brought out that fact in relation to clinical material. Glover, especially, emphasized that the central conflict of the fetishist dates back to the earliest oral phase.

With two fetishists, whose therapy was successful to the extent of their marrying and leading a normal heterosexual life, I could clearly trace the development of their perversion back to pre-phallic and oral experiences. Outstanding separation anxiety, the desire to cling to the mother, were elicited constantly in the therapeutic process, the mother always being a phallic mother—and the phallus, at the same time, being represented by the early desired breast. This then resulted in identification with the mother—an identification which also served to eliminate castration anxiety. One patient used as a fetish for his sexual gratification the female leg, orginally just looking at it and, in the course of therapy, fondling and rubbing it. This was the revival of an actual infantile experience. The next stage in the therapy was to make him dare to approach a woman more directly and find a compliant partner who was permissive and who reassured him by letting him practice his sexual gratification by rubbing her leg. Gradually—partly through this actual experience of contact with a woman and mainly through further analysis—he reached full sexual maturity and married.

This problem of oral deprivation—feelings of resentment resulting in castration anxiety—can also be noted as the central struggle in the homosexual. With the fetishist, the fetish is not only a defense against castration fear but also a protection from externalizing aggression against the mother's breast; identification with the mother is a further protection against hating the mother. We see, in the homosexual, the same mechanism—identification with the loved-hated object.

The male homosexual identifies with the mother and turns away from the heterosexual object; in this manner, his original aggression against the mother is eliminated. This mechanism is also present in the female homosexual; she turns away from the corrupt, seductive superego and identifies with the parent of the opposite sex, thereby eliminating the destructive tendencies against him. Sometimes, at the developmental phase of puberty, patients whose ego structure is too weak for the struggle of adjustment to sexuality will be pushed into choosing the homosexual path when exposed to the seductiveness of the parent of the opposite sex. For example, the parent who indulges in sexual jokes with the adolescent youngster or who slaps the youngster playfully on various parts of the body will communicate permission for sexual phantasies about that parent; this, in turn, creates panic and leads to flight from the whole problem of heterosexuality in the direction of homosexuality.

The unconscious wish to suck and to incorporate the breast of the pre-Oedipal mother appears in the form of sucking the penis—which constitutes both a denial and an unconscious gratification of the oral desire in the male homosexual. Being sucked gratifies the unconscious drive to be identified with the mother. These unconscious desires appear in the *phantasy life* of the homosexual and illuminate the problems involved in therapy.

Ferenczi was the first to emphasize the fact that homosexuality and perversion, in a great number of cases, constitute a symptomatic formation—a prophylactic or creative device. They appear as a defense, a way of overcoming the anxiety connected with the opposite sex. He was also of the opinion that "homosexuality gains its significance from the content of unconscious phantasy which is realized in the perversion." I found this statement of great importance in the treatment of patients. The minute examination of their perverse practices proved to be an "acting out" of drives and phantasies—infantile and polymorphous-perverse in character. Equally important for therapy is the problem of early anxieties and guilt feelings attached to the perverse gratification.

A paper by Anna Freud, read at the International Psychoanalytic Congress in Zurich, 1949, and entitled *Some Clinical Remarks Concerning the Treatment of Some Cases of Male Homosexuality*, contains a contribution which has been valuable in the therapy of male homosexuals. She suggested that "the basis for classification should not be the overt practice carried out with a partner but the phantasy which accompanies the act (identification with the active or passive partner respectively)." Her suggested approach toward a different classification of homosexuality, not on the basis of the manifest perversion but on the basis of conscious or unconscious phantasies which accompany the homosexual act, is important in the therapeutic management of perversions.

Ferenczi described a fundamental difference between the "active" and "passive" type of homosexual. In his opinion, the "passive" type does not seek treatment, being satisfied with his role. The "active" type is more aware of and disturbed by his abnormality and tries to change. Ferenczi regarded the "passive" type as incurable by analysis. But, as he put it: "We can influence his behavior, remove any neurotic symptom which may accompany the inversion, especially morbid anxiety."

The "active" type Ferenczi considered a typical "obsessional neurotic"—one whose homosexuality is compulsion. He described therapeutic success on a transference basis even in a short time. But he felt that the slightest conflict would make the patient relapse and real analysis must then begin. He doubted the possibility of a complete cure although, in a number of cases, he achieved "far-reaching improvement." The improvement was mostly in reducing his patients' hostility toward women, better control of homosexual acting out and increasing sexual desire toward women. These successes led him to hope that a thoroughgoing cure would someday be possible.

The more primitive the perversion, the nearer it is to the source of the original anxiety—that early infantile anxiety which is present in all perversions and which is reanimated and exacerbated in the adult life of perverse persons. From the therapeutic point of view, this early anxiety has great significance. The extension of data on this subject and that of infantile sexuality in general, and the growing appreciation of the role played by early frustrations and aggressive reactions have been useful in the approach to the therapy of perversions. It can be clearly demonstrated that, behind the fear of heterosexuality, there was once a very strong attachment to the heterosexual object. The strong resistance to heterosexuality which we find will, through a slow process, be amenable to reduction and to change. Naturally, this will come about only when the resistances of the patient become centralized during the analytic process in the relationship to the analyst and when all the reactions to early frustrations and intimidations, as well as all the strong fixations to the heterosexual object, are re-experienced and then given up in therapeutic setting.

A young man, an overt homosexual, came to analysis because of shame and embarrassment over his homosexual activities, confusion in his studies and feelings of inferiority in relation to his friends. He expressed indifference toward the opposite sex. In analysis, his attention was directed to the fact that he was very much interested in his little sister, whom he wanted to protect from their mother's aggression. This fact and the minute and detailed investigation of his relationship to this sister—and, through her, to other girls—brought up more new facts which he had tried to deny—his many reactions and feelings about women. These feelings, phantasies, thoughts, and behavior toward women played a very important part in his analysis for many months. Through them we were able to direct his attention to his relationship with his parents and, especially, to his earliest feelings about his mother. This period of therapy involved much conscious work on his part, thinking about and elaborating on his thoughts and phantasies; it led him to take up once more the relationships with girls which he had abandoned at puberty.

He was a serious, extremely good-looking young man, a good dancer and a good actor, and he was very much appreciated by girls. He began to go to dances, to the theatre and to parties where he was in constant contact with girls. One of the girls, who showed some understanding and was somewhat motherly in her approach to him, seduced him. They undressed and spent nights together, which he enjoyed very much; however, he could never consummate intercourse. He had the following dream shortly after such a night: "I am wandering around in the dark and I find myself in a room filled with mannikins. They surround me; they want to dance with me; they want to have fun with me. I scream and run away."

During this period, all his castration anxieties and rivalries with his father, and his possible shame and embarrassment with women, were again and again minutely discussed and investigated. His attention was drawn to all the relevant implications of his frequent masturbation. At one time, for instance, the analytical hour proceeded as follows. He had masturbated, after having been with the girl, and came to the analytic session very much upset. The rest of the hour consisted of his trying to associate and explain in a conscious, logical way his behavior just prior to coming for his treatment session. He could not understand why he was so upset. He had planned to masturbate and, after all, he is an adult and can do what he wishes. "But why did I do it? Why couldn't I control it? Why do I feel in that respect like a helpless child?" He challenged his own answers to these questions again and again. "What did I want to accomplish by it?" *These ego investigations* brought up very strong aggressive feelings in relation to his parents and to me. I could then interpret to him the ramification of his conflicts at every phase of his development and also the reason *for his acting out*, which masturbation represented at that point.

Instead of deep and frequent interpretation, understanding of his conscious behavior was the immediate object of investigation, followed later by deep interpretation. There was a constant effort to mobilize his feelings and the phantasies which accompanied his homosexual contacts and his masturbation. The working through always followed a developmental line back from the homosexual practices to the earliest oral phase; the patient's ego interest was directed to a minute investigation of all that he aimed at in his perversion and in the *acting out of his perverse phantasies and drives.*

Many of his phantasies were about sucking and being sucked. "You [the therapist] have a breast, normal size on the left breast; then it grows bigger and bigger like a big wall; then it becomes my [the patient's] breast."

For him, the word "sucking" was a repulsive word, most difficult to mention. It reminded him of fears of choking; and yet, he enjoyed the phantasy of being sucked. It was a long struggle to recognize all these oral problems which manifested themselves in so many ways. There was a gradual recognition and a periodic acting out of the various oral tendencies, always combined with aggressiveness. Behind this acting out was hidden great dependence on and need for support from the therapist who represented both parents, but primarily the mother.

He had sexual contacts with a classmate—an athletic young Negro who performed fellatio on him. The patient passively enjoyed the act. It appeared, in analysis, that he chose this partner because of his athletic build and his identification with him. This identification he tried to hide and deny behind the *color* of his sexual partner. The latter's huge penis was an important factor; in choosing him he realized, by identification, his desire to acquire that powerful organ.

He gradually dropped his passivity in the transference relationship, becoming more and more aggressive. He also changed his generally passive attitude toward his parents and friends and in social life; after a time, he became more interested in girls.

He was aggressive with his male partners in sex contact—he called it masculine—but the mother-identification was outstanding. At a later period in analysis, he phantasied having sexual relations with girls. These phantasies frightened him because they were predominantly sadistic; he behaved in them as he would with a man but with the thought that such action would injure a woman. His fear of women was attached solely to sexual contact; otherwise, he was more in their company than in men's. His unconscious guilt feelings were also due to genital phantasies—phantasies which dealt with ways of achieving satisfaction.

His masculine pride was misdirected. It appeared as an attitude of defiance, especially in the presence of his father or some father-image. He had to recognize that pride and defiance were two different things. When it came to a situation where aggressiveness was called for, he felt weak and cowardly. He soon recognized that the cause of this was the identification with his mother.

When his homosexual system was disturbed and his heterosexual interest became more obvious to him, he developed many hysterical symptoms—partly involving his genitals, such as a rash, and herpes which troubled him for a considerable period—in order to interfere with his progress toward heterosexuality. These symptoms brought to the foreground his preoccupation with sexual problems and offered an opportunity to work through once more the pregenital phases of his development when he had suffered from similar physical afflictions.

From the beginning of his analysis, he kept insisting that his aim and desire was to be married. His active tendencies were strong in his social life; the passive ones played a role only in his sexual orientation and here, also, only partially.

His oversensitivity was connected with that passivity and it led us to his very early experiences which we could follow back to the age of two and a half or three. They were traumatic in nature because of the shifting attitude of mother, nurse and grandmother, the three women who "spoiled" him and, at the same time, "dominated" him. Indeed, the analysis moved around these three women, to whom later was added a sister.

The analysis of his early emotional relationship with these women repeatedly brought to light the vicissitudes of his Oedipal struggle. Naturally, the attachments, frustrations and fears of the pregenital phase of his development precipitated the strong emotional tone of the Oedipal relationship and the post-Oedipal conflicts. His ego was crippled at an early age. All this initiated his strong castration fears—still present in adolescence —and resulted in perversion as a defense and a denial.

A female homosexual of twenty-two came to analysis because of depressive moods and aggressive attitudes toward her parents and in her social life (which was also, by the way, her defense against femininity). Her phantasies and dreams about competition with men and rejection of the feminine role were constantly in the center of the therapy. A few of her dreams will illustrate her problems. She dreamed: "I was lying on the couch, being analyzed. You [the doctor] said that I should masturbate. I began to have an erection. I had a penis. The erection was not very big. Then I turned my penis backward and pushed it into my vagina." Another dream: "Sister and brother are getting married to each other. Both left their girl and boy friend, respectively." A third dream: "I left my husband; so did my girl friend. We discussed how she hated her husband and I was glad that she too, hated men."

During her homosexual activities, she had phantasies about a man, in which she would visualize his penis, and also about marriage and having babies. She awoke from a dream one night with vaginal sensations; the dream was as follows: "A baby of about two or three was crawling around on my body, in bed." She talked about the large nipples on her breasts and their capacity to become erected. When the desires for men, dates and sex contact with men became stronger, she fought them with regressive phantasies, her dreams especially revealing anxieties about heterosexuality.

She reported the following dream: "I played with Father's penis and my girl friend was looking on." This dream had an obvious source in the fact that, as far back as she remembered, she had seen her father, if not nude, at least in transparent underclothing; she had always been aware of his genitals. The girl friend who appeared in the dream was her partner in sexual practices and many of the patient's dreams centered around her; most of the time, she represented the mother figure with whom the patient was in competition.

Another time, she phantasied herself standing on the street with her breasts exposed. A man is looking out of a window. Her left breast is pointing up toward the man; she does all kinds of tricks with it. In her sexual contact with her girl friend, she imagined herself being a passive child and her friend making love to her, kissing her and playing the role of either mother or father. At other times, they rubbed each other's bodies, involving also the clitoris, and played with each other's breasts. During the course of analysis, the bisexual phantasies in her sexual play gradually became stronger, leading her to an overemphasis on heterosexuality; for instance, she would go to bed and phantasy about a penis with hair but without a man's body attached to it. More phantasies followed, aggressive in nature, such as tearing out a man's penis when she was angry; they were succeeded by phantasies of running away with girl friends. Her phantasies were frequently of adolescent character and very involved, dealing with orgies, sexual acts in which a number of people—always both men and women—took part. In the process of treatment, her masturbatory phantasies became more and more heterosexual.

Her need to convince herself, and others, that she was homosexual had the unconscious aim of avoiding aggression against her father and, with it, the ensuing guilt. She tried, with her homosexual behavior, to convince him that she was a loving daughter (she was the more anxious to do this because he had a mistress and was, thus, unfaithful to his wife) and would always love only him (not wanting to marry any other man). At the same time, her homosexuality was an appeasement of her mother—convincing her that she hated men (as mother hated father) and that she did not want any of them. This helped her to render unconscious her jealousy and hatred of her mother and to avoid fear and guilt in relation to her.

As every perversion is mixed with different neurotic symptomatology—sometimes one and sometimes the other being in the foreground—the therapeutic aim will also shift at times. In addition, we have to consider in therapy the possible changes which we feel the patient is capable of attaining. Attention must thus constantly be paid to ego strength, to tolerance of frustration. This latter factor is sometimes the cause of analysts' refusal to treat homosexuals; the therapist frequently feels that the patient will have to give up his perverse practices during the period of analysis and that the patient will not be able to tolerate this abstinence from sexuality. Homosexuals are also frequently considered incapable of complying with the basic rules of analysis.

The symptoms which reflect the perverse behavior of the patient are rooted in behavior patterns established at various levels of development; thus, the various aspects of infantile development—attachments, frustrations, anxieties and fixations—must be kept constantly in focus during therapy. In order to bring about a reduction of the defenses, to eliminate symptoms, and to establish a better adult functioning, we have to make more direct use of our knowledge of the ego.

Some writers emphasize the need for "active interference" in certain periods of analysis, especially when the patient's transference is strong enough so that he will accept and carry out active suggestions. I never interfere actively, especially not with patients' sexual behavior. At times, naturally, it is necessary to interfere by analysis, and even by positive suggestion with the patient's general behavior; as, for instance, I was obliged to do with one of my patients who had a tendency to be belligerent and fought openly with his father. What I mean by "ego-direction" in analysis is bringing such ego-reactions to the patient's attention.

Such an explosive attitude is, naturally, a repetition of early infantile reactions to the love object; it serves as a defense against unconscious infantile pregenital tendencies and their accompanying early anxieties. Just as the explosive aggression against the father, in the case just described, served as a defense measure against the patient's attachment and identification with his father, so did his sexual behavior serve the same purpose; this, however, referred to his mother, with whom he had a deep identification through which he managed to repress castration anxiety. This latter problem—the identification with mother—was in constant focus during the analytical process, because it was the patient's strongest defensive measure and, at the same time, the means of leading him back to heterosexual interest and, later, normal sexuality.

There is sufficient reason, in the case of certain types of perversions, to deviate from the regular procedure which we are accustomed to follow in the therapy of neurosis. These modifications in our technical approach will always depend on the patient's problems and on the type of perversion from which he suffers. These modifications, incidentally, are evident in the few technical references published about the therapy of perversions. The variety and strength of perverse practices in the patients and the nature of their symptoms are, of course, determined by their pregenital character and fixations.

The defense mechanisms against heterosexuality, which institute regression with the advance of sexual drives, will place the emphasis of gratification on *those libidinally charged partial drives which constitute fixation in the course of development. In other words, the partial sexual drive which has been most highly cathected will be carried over in later phases of development and sexual gratification will be achieved through these partial sexual drives.*

In the therapy of perverse patients, one is struck most of all by their ever-present phantasies in which the desire to be happy, admired, loved, and to achieve gratification by any means they can, is clearly represented. Their manner of sexual gratification is a circuitous way of achieving orgastic pleasure—a kind of substitute for normal heterosexual genital contact. This is especially true of the major perversions where it is obvious, from the patients' phantasies and dreams, that they really seek sexual contact with the opposite sex. The sexual goal of the homosexual is always to achieve a phallic orgasm. His contact with his object in the sexual act will be that of manipulation, as if he were having intercourse, with accompanying phantasies identifying with the partner in masculine or feminine role. The female homosexual, likewise, will seek a substitute for the phallus to get sexual gratification and will achieve vaginal orgasm by identification with the partner in masculine or feminine role.

Perverts cannot face open contact with the genital of the opposite sex; they have to mask it and convince themselves that their way of gratification is superior to the frankly heterosexual act. They want to maintain their sexual standards and they seem quite naïve. They may call their particular form of perversion "super sex," as did one of my patients who also called himself "superman" in telling me about his way of sexual gratification.

In analysis, they very soon become aware of their basic desire for the heterosexual love partner. At the same time, they begin to see clearly why they pursue happiness through perverse channels. They realize what a great amount of frustration, aggressivity, anxiety and guilt was attached to their first heterosexual love objects in infancy and childhood; this is what is still at work in their unconscious, making them consciously distort the sexual reality.

Their perversion is an expression of the whole personality structure. Their phantasy life has to be explored and exposed; this will help them to recognize and accept the fact that their way of seeking gratification is a defense and a flight from their deepest desire, heterosexuality.

REFERENCES

Blanton, S. "Phallic Women." *Psychoanalytic Quarterly*, Vol. XVI, 1947.

Bryan, D. "Bisexuality." *International Journal of Psychoanalysis*, Vol. XI, 1930.

———. "Circumcision and Problems of Bisexuality." *International Journal of Psychoanalysis*, Vol. XXVIII, 1947.

Bychowski, G. "The Ego of Homosexuals." *International Journal of Psychoanalysis*, Vol. XXVI, 1945.

Freeman, T. "Clinical and Theoretical Observations on Male Homosexuality." *International Journal of Psychoanalysis*, Vol. XXXVI, 1955.

Freud, A. "Some Clinical Remarks Concerning the Treatment of Cases of Male Homosexuality." *International Journal of Psychoanalysis*, Vol. XXX, 1949.

Freud, S. "Certain Neurotic Mechanisms in Jealousy, Paranoia and Homosexuality." *Coll Papers*, Vol. II. London, 1924.

―――. *Inhibitions, Symptoms and Anxiety.* London, 1936.

―――. *Three Essays on the Theory of Sexuality.* London, 1949.

―――. "Psychogenesis of a Case of Female Homosexuality." *Coll. Papers*, Vol. II. London, 1924.

Gillespie, W. H. "Notes on the Analysis of Sexual Perversions." *International Journal of Psychoanalysis*, Vol. XXXIII, 1952.

Glover, E. "The Relation of Perversion Formation to the Development of Reality Sense." *International Journal of Psychoanalysis*, Vol. XIV, 1933.

Glover, J. "Notes on an Unusual Form of Perversion." *International Journal of Psychoanalysis*, Vol. VIII, 1927.

Jones, C. W. S. "A Case of War Shock Resulting from Sex Inversion." *International Journal of Psychoanalysis*, Vol. I, 1920.

Lagache, E. "Homosexuality and Jealousy." *International Journal of Psychoanalysis*, Vol. XXXI, 1950.

Lampl-de Groot, J. "The Pre-Oedipal Phase in the Development of the Male Child." *The Psychoanalytic Study of the Child*, Vol. I. New York, 1946.

Lewinsky, H. "Notes on Two Special Features in a Homosexual Patient." *International Journal of Psychoanalysis*, Vol. XXX, 1949.

Lorand, S. "Bisexuality." *The Morbid Personality.* New York, 1931.

―――. "Contribution to the Problem of Vaginal Orgasm." *Clinical Studies in Psychoanalysis.* New York, 1950.

―――. "Fetishism in Statu Nascendi." *International Journal of Psychoanalysis*, Vol. XI, 1930.

―――. "Perverse Tendencies and Fantasies: their influence on personality." *Clinical Studies in Psychoanalysis.* New York, 1950.

―――. "Psycho-Sexual Infantilism." *The Morbid Personality.* New York, 1931.

Nunberg, H. "Homosexuality, Magic and Aggression." *International Journal of Psychoanalysis*, Vol. XIX, 1938.

Robbins, B. "Psychological Implications of the Male Homosexual." *Psychoanalytic Review*, Vol. XXX, 1943.

Sadger, J. "A Contribution to the Understanding of Sadomasochism." *International Journal of Psychoanalysis*, Vol. VII, 1926.

Thorner, H. A. "Notes on a Case of Male Homosexuality." *International Journal of Psychoanalysis*, Vol. XXX, 1949.

Wittels, F. "Collective Defense Mechanisms Against Homosexuality." *Psychoanalytic Review*, Vol. XXXI, 1944.

————. "Mona Lisa and Feminine Beauty: a study in bisexuality." *International Journal of Psychoanalysis*, Vol. XV, 1934.

Wulff, M. "A Case of Male Homosexuality." *International Journal of Psychoanalysis*, Vol. XXIII, 1942.